三幕舞台劇

泣血煙花

姜龍昭 著

蔣娉 譯

國立中央圖書館出版品預行編目資料

泣血煙花：三幕舞臺劇 = Angels in hell :
an original play / 姜龍昭著 ; 蔣娉譯. --
初版. -- 臺北市：文史哲，民81
面 ；　公分
ISBN 957-547-185-7(平裝)

854.6　　　　　　　　　　　81006561

泣血煙花

著　　者：姜　　龍　　　昭

出版者：文　史　哲　出　版　社

登記證字號：行政院新聞局局版臺業字五三三七號

發行人：彭　　　　正　　雄

發行所：文　史　哲　出　版　社

印刷者：文　史　哲　出　版　社
台北市羅斯福路一段七十二巷四號
郵撥〇五一二八八一二彭正雄帳戶
電話：三　五　一　一　〇　二　八

中華民國八十一年十二月初版

實價新台幣二四〇元

自序

距今五十年前，我在大陸蘇州唸高中的時候，讀過一本劇作家曹禺寫的舞臺劇本：「日出」，劇中有一個十五、六歲死了父母的「小東西」，因受不了妓院黑社會的欺凌，在第三幕中上吊自殺了，那一幕，他寫的十分深入，那慘不忍睹的情景，迄今仍給我留下難以泯滅的印象。

那時候，對一些未成年的妓女，叫做：「童娼」。

想不到，事隔五十年後，在富庶的寶島臺灣，在報紙上依然能看到一些未成年的少女，因淪入煙花巷中，受盡種種的迫害，只是改了個名稱，叫「雛妓」，本省人則稱之為「幼齒」。

最先，這些雛妓，多半來自山地鄉，後來，自民國七十六年開放以後，一些偷渡來臺的大陸少女，也被人肉販子掌握，送入了「火坑」。臺北雖有一些慈善團體，如「婦女救援基金會」等機構，努力救援，但對那些淪入風塵的女性，依然有力不從心之感。

據臺北市政府的調查，都市中有五成以上的男性，都曾去過風月場所，百分之八二‧七六嫖妓的原因，是商業應酬、及滿足個人好奇、娛樂、尋找刺激、解決性慾等因素。

一

近年來，由於嫖客的性偏差所為、戀童症（Pedophiliu）、求愛障礙（Courtship disorder）情有獨鍾，造成、自卑心理，以及中國人「滋補且少性病」的錯誤認知，對一些未成年的「雛妓」，情有獨鍾，造成了「雛妓市場」的格外興旺。

我國的刑法明文規定：：「姦淫未滿十四歲之女子，以強姦論」、「姦淫十四歲以上，未滿十六歲之女子為姦淫幼女罪」，但都是告訴乃論，對嫖客而言，實難有實質遏阻的效果。

不久以前，在內政部的支持下，勵馨基金會，對臺北市的「雛妓」完成了一項調查，分析未成年的少女，做這種「行業」的原因如下：：

一、由朋友介紹者：：達百分之三〇‧三。

二、被逼出賣的：：佔百分之二一‧二。

三、看報紙應徵工作陷入火坑者：：佔百分之二〇‧二。

從上述統計中，可以看出，真正出於自願者，所佔的百分比並不多。

「雛妓」的問題，不僅是五十年前的大陸有，五十年後的臺灣有，在菲律賓、泰國等落後地區，也有「童妓」的存在，據報紙記載，菲律賓警方，在逮捕的嫖客中發現，有不少是外來的觀光客。其中有十三名美國人，六名德國人，四個英國人。因為菲律賓人貧苦眾多，統計僅首都馬尼拉一地，童妓就有兩萬人之多，據說有些父母對子女為「童妓」，已麻木無所謂，有一對十二、九歲的姐妹，還在母親的陪同下，前往皮條客指定的旅館，做賣淫的勾當。

可見，賣淫的行為，不僅中國有，其他國家也有，是有國際性的。

七十九年十月，我多方蒐羅資料，完成了這個劇本的初稿，並未出版。到了八十一年初，曾將之改編成廣播劇，分上、下兩集，在中廣公司播出，及後在請蔣娉女士翻譯的過程中，蒙她的求好心切，又仔細的一改再改，修了二次，如今配合譯成之英文，出版了此一中英對照本。劇名在英文譯名方面，我接受了蔣娉的意見，定名為「地獄天使」（Angels in Hell）意在述說一群可愛的「天使」，不幸落入「地獄」，受盡諸種殘酷辛酸的迫害與折磨。

蔣娉女士、旅美廿多年，畢業於美國紐澤西州瑞格士大學道格拉斯女子學院（Douglaes College Rutgers University American Studies B.A），對於戲劇，尤具深切的研究，她曾翻譯過我的「淚水的沉思」、「飛機失事以後」，這是她翻譯的第三個劇本，譯筆益見流暢成熟。

在翻譯的過程中，她主動提供了不少寶貴的意見，讓我修正。她認為這個劇本的故事，深深令她熱血沸騰，為求其國際化，永恆化，突破時間、空間的限制，因此部份對白，她採用「意譯」，不使用中文之地名，因為不僅臺北有華西街，北投有杏花閣，其他國家，也有相類似的地方，這一點，是我需要在此說明的的。

其次，我要聲明感謝的，是蔣娉女士的先生John Sowyer Moxon，不特在翻譯時為本劇作了細心的校正，更難得的是他為本劇寫了英文的序言。我衷心盼望，本劇在世界劇壇上能有英文演出的一天。

　這一次的封面圖樣，仍由中國電視公司的美術組長邱則明先生與美術設計師楊紀迪小姐，共同精心設計，並蒙美術設計師賴鎭遠題字，使畫面呈現了悠美的典雅色彩與風格。

　凡有意演出本劇之團體，希尊重著作權，演出前，先函臺灣臺北市八德路三段十二巷五七弄十九號四樓，或電話：（○二）七一一五八二○號徵得本人之同意。演出時，註明編劇及譯者姓名，勿任意改動對白及情節。若公開售票作營業性之演出，盼能酌付作者演出版權費，改編爲電影、電視、廣播劇，則事先徵求作者之意願。

　　　　　　　　　　　　　　　　　姜龍昭　寫於民國八十一年十二月四日

蔣娉與作者合影

「泣血煙花」

（三幕舞臺劇）

人物表：

小　文——一個年十五歲的小雛妓，因着父親的好賭，使之淪入風塵，受盡迫害。

許彩玉——一個個性倔強，苦學好勝的女孩子，因遇人不淑，被騙賣入妓女戶，為了反抗，最後自己結束了痛苦的一生，十七、八歲。

如　花——身世悲淒的貧家女，在各種不同的色情場所均有工作過，能逆來忍受，年十七歲。

賴　桑——年四十餘歲，妓女戶的老闆娘，心狠手辣，凌虐那些妓女，一副十足的老鴇面孔。

邱阿坤——孔武有力，體格魁梧，是妓女戶的保鏢，助紂為虐，做盡壞事，卅歲左右。

石三郎——小文的父親，為想發財，賭昏了頭，做出一些犯法的而又違反人性的事來，為了錢，近四十歲。

黑　皮——一個流氓兼嫖客，是老闆娘賴桑的狎友，走私大陸妹及黑槍進口，為了錢，什麼壞事，都可以做，年四十餘歲。

阿福婆——年已五十許，仍要打扮，三姑六婆型的女性，也暗地經營一些色情勾當。

巧　妹——愛慕虛榮，自大陸來臺的女孩，十七、八歲，不識字，頭腦簡單，身材姣好。

小　毛——比巧妹，年輕兩歲，也不識字，有點天眞，不願接受侮辱，有她的可愛處。

高警員——奉公守法，妓女戶的管區女警員，職位不高，但不貪污，絕對公事公辦，上場穿女性警察制服。

姚老師——一個卅餘歲，補校的女老師，愛護學生的教育工作者，對弱者有同情心，救援却有無力感。

時間：

第一幕——民國七十八年六月間的某一天。

第二幕——距第一幕一個多月以後。

第三幕——距第二幕一段時日後的下午。

地點：

臺北華西街某一妓女戶

布景：

舞臺上，共分兩個景區。

一個景是妓女戶的堂屋，有沙發、茶几、矮櫃、電話、辦公桌等陳設。另有電鈴等裝置。

正面對觀眾部份，有一窗戶，可看見窗外景色，是白天或是夜晚，可穿插華西街車來人往的熙擾聲音。

有門簾，一通外面大門，一通內屋。

另一個景是妓女的房間，採用塌塌米日本式紙拉門也可，或者是簡單的雙人床、衣櫥、及簡單的茶几沙發椅，有門通外面。

堂屋與臥室，用抽象式景片隔開，或是僅用燈光之變化，來表示，是兩個並立的不同景區，務使觀眾能夠接受。

劇情簡介

臺北華西街的妓女戶，是都市中，最骯髒的角落。

隨着社會脈動的急驟演變，有些女孩子，如許彩玉，被騙賣到這兒來，有些因家庭環境的影響，如小文、如花，被逼迫到這兒來，受盡折磨與屈辱，過着痛苦的皮肉生涯。

自政府開放大陸探親後，一些不法之徒，如黑皮者流，由大陸騙來一些無知的姑娘如巧妹、小毛，來這兒賣淫。雛妓、大陸妹的猖獗，造成社會道德的淪喪，大家都在向錢看齊，笑貧不笑娼，有心人如姚老師者，雖想伸出援手，却有無力之感。

隨着色情買賣、無恥勾當的盛行，走私偷渡，賭博綁票，相繼發生，是社會惡勢力的結合，形成現代社會的毒瘤，已不容我們再容忍，視若無睹。

本劇為了使大家認清近年來，都市角落醜惡的一面，僅以客觀的筆觸，素描這些罪惡的形形色色，暴露呈現在大眾面前，希冀，在辛酸的關注中，引起你對未來的探討與反省。

四

第一幕

時：六月間，一個炎熱夏天的下午

景：妓女戶的堂屋及臥室

人：許彩玉、小文、如花、賴桑、邱阿坤、石三郎、高警員、黑皮、阿福婆

幕啓時：

窗外，映射進來一片紅色的晚霞。

堂屋裡賴坐着生氣，她一手拿扇子，又用手帕擦汗，稍頃，抽起煙來。臥室裡，小文縮在角落裡坐着發楞，一臉恐怖的神色。

稍頃，幕後，響起一陣皮鞭的抽打聲，許彩玉，痛澈心肺的嚎叫着，只聞其聲，不見其人。

彩玉：（幕後）你打好了，你打死我，也不會答應你的！

賴：（對着後面門吼叫）好，……阿坤，給我用力打，看是她硬，還是，我硬！……

阿坤：（幕後）是！（用力的鞭打聲）

賴：（在臺上走來走去）到了我這兒來，不聽我的，就是自找苦吃！……惹火了我，……看我不敢從

「泣血煙花」

五

彩玉：你身上剝下一層皮來！……

彩玉：（頑強的）你休想要我答應你去接客，做這種不要臉的事，我情願死，你打死我好了！

賴：（自說自話）我才捨不得讓你去死呢？……我只是修理修理，讓你知道我的厲害！（對後吼叫）

阿坤，別用鞭子抽了！用香煙頭燙她的手掌心！

阿坤：是！（停止鞭打，不久，煙頭燙手心的慘叫聲，自幕後傳出）

小文：（在場上，也被嚇得跳起來，啼哭不已）啊！……

（突然，靜寂下來）

賴：怎麼啦？阿坤。

阿坤：昏過去了！……

賴：用水噴醒，送她回房去，餓她三天，不給飯吃，看她還聽不聽話！（賴倒水喝，坐下抽煙搧扇子）

（噴水聲，甦醒聲，鬆綁聲，開門聲，臥室門打開，彩玉滿身傷痕的被推了進來，阿坤進入臥室

，像老鷹抓小雞似的，把小文一把抓出臥室。）

阿坤：小文，現在輪到你了，走吧！……

（阿坤把小文拉出後，重又把門關好，鎖上，彩玉撫摸着四肢，痛苦的哭泣起來）

（幕後又傳出一頓皮鞭抽打聲）

賴：問她肯不肯聽話？接客？不肯的話，……阿坤，你給我用力的打，……我就不相信，你們的皮肉，會不怕痛！

小文：老闆娘，求你別打了，……我……受不了了，……我聽話，答應你接客，就是了。求求你，放過了我吧！

阿坤：是！

賴：答應接客就別打了，……阿坤，給她鬆綁，饒了她這一次。

花：老闆娘（向之行禮）我回來了。

（這時，如花臉色憔悴的自通外面大門回來，上場）

賴：如花，你才去沒有一會兒，怎麼這麼快，就回來啦？

花：那個老風流，還沒有幾秒鐘就完事了，我也沒辦法。

賴：真沒用。（伸手向花）錢哪？

花：（自口袋中，拿出一疊鈔票，還有一些零錢交給賴）都在這兒。

賴：（將錢數了一下說）快樂賓館服務生電話話裡說好，休息壹次一千元，怎麼這兒只有八百元呢？

花：賓館的服務生，扣去兩百元，是規費，我可一毛錢也沒有拿。

賴：哦！（拿出五十元給花）如花，這五十元給你零用。

「泣血煙花」

花：謝謝老闆娘。（接過錢）我進去清洗一下。（走向內屋）

賴：等一等，你過來。

（花只能折回，走向賴）

賴：你讓我檢查一下。（賴先檢查花的口袋，無所獲）把鞋子脫下。（花脫下鞋襪，賴仔細檢查沒有查到，又檢查她頭髮上的蝴蝶結，也沒有查到什麼，最後伸手入她的奶罩，終於找出摺成很小的一張鈔票，打開一看是張百元鈔票）

（花神情沮喪）

賴：你藏在奶罩裡，就以爲我找不到了！（狠狠出手猛摑花一個耳光）下次，再讓我發現，你藏私房錢，小心，我就讓你脫光了衣服遊街！

花：（哭泣，撫摸被打的臉）老闆娘，這不是私房錢，是客人另外賞給我的「小費」。

賴：小費，……你還想要「小費」，我告訴你，什麼費，都得交給我，聽清楚了沒有？你是我化錢買來的！……你身上的一塊肉，一根毛，都是我的！……要不是我比較「好心」，你一塊零用錢，也休想有，知道嗎？

花：是，老闆娘。

賴：對了，你剛才出去的時候，你的男朋友，叫什麼陳添丁的，來找你，……你不在，他就走了！……他和我說，他要娶你，和你結婚，是眞的還是假的？

八

花：他……真的很愛我，……他說他現在在當兵，等服完了兵役，……他就和他的父母說，要替我贖

賴：他家裡很有錢嗎？

花：他家在南部，有很多「地」，最近賣了一些，蓋房子，賺了不少錢，我想，他不會騙我的！

賴：如花，眼睛睜大一點，男人的話，十句不一定靠得住一句，……這年頭，什麼都是假的，只有「鈔票」，才是真的！

花：老闆娘，你放心，添丁若是沒有錢，我是不會偷偷跟他跑了的，你放心就是了！

賴：嗯，……你能這樣想，就好了！……做人，最要緊的是不能忘恩負義，過河拆橋！……你在我這兒上班，我可沒有虧待你唷！

花：是，老闆娘。

賴：好了，你進去清洗吧，說不定，一會兒，又有生意上門。

花：是。（進入內屋，下場）

（阿坤押著小文自內屋走出）

阿坤：賴桑，小文她口渴，想喝水。……（把口中的檳榔吐掉，像一口血水）

賴：又沒有繩子綁着你，要喝水，自己不會去倒。

小文：是，老闆娘。（她臉上身上均有鞭打的血跡，她步履蹣跚的走向矮櫃，去倒茶水來喝着）

「泣血煙花」

九

賴：阿坤，⋯⋯有我在這兒，她跑不掉的，⋯⋯你沒事，還是去大門口守着。

阿坤：是。（向通外大門口走去，下場）

賴：小文，⋯⋯來，⋯⋯坐下。⋯⋯還是你肯聽話，⋯⋯那個彩玉，真是賤，不修理修理，發瘋似的。跟我來鬥，⋯⋯還有好日子她過的嗎？⋯⋯我現在把她關在黑屋子裡，餓她三天三夜，⋯⋯你看她還叫不叫饒！

小文：老闆娘，我給你做下女，行不行？洗廁所，燒飯，擦地板，我什麼都做，只求你，別讓我接客，⋯⋯好不好？

賴：怎麼？你剛才答應了我，現在又反悔啦？⋯⋯你不怕，我用香煙頭，來燙你的手掌心！

小文：老闆娘，我不是反悔，⋯⋯我只是不想做這樣下賤的事，⋯⋯是彩玉說的，⋯⋯她說，⋯⋯接客，會使人墮落，讓別人瞧不起！

賴：（發出可怕的笑聲）嘿！⋯⋯嘿！⋯⋯。墮落，⋯⋯沒有錢，才會墮落，⋯⋯小文，你爸，要不是為了背債，會把你賣給我嗎？⋯⋯

小文：老闆娘，我還小，今年才十五歲，⋯⋯等我長大了，⋯⋯再幫你賺錢，好不好？

賴：你爸賣你的時候，就親口告訴我說，兩年前，你曾經給人強暴過，⋯⋯那一次，還去派出所報過案，⋯⋯現在，你已經長大了，又不是頭一次，還有什麼好怕的呢？

小文：老闆娘，⋯⋯（低頭沉默了一下，才說）我要為你做多久？

賴：你爸給我訂的契約上，寫得很清楚，他沒有告訴你？

小文：沒有，我爸，他什麼也沒有說，只要我乖乖的躲在這兒，……聽你的話，要我做什麼，……你就做什麼？

賴：你爸拿了我卅五萬塊錢，契約上寫明你得給我做上五年，讓我把本錢和利錢，賺回來以後，你才能夠走路。

小文：五年，……這麼久，……那我都可以考大學了！

賴：怎麼？你覺得太長了？我告訴你，有人還要在我這兒待一輩子呢？你今年十五歲，五年以後，正好廿歲，還年輕得很，你若願意留下來，我們四六拆賬，……可以幫你賺不少錢喔，……放心，……照樣會有人願意娶你去做太太的！

小文：我才不想這麼多，……老闆娘，一天，我要接幾次客？

賴：這可很難說，你若對客人好一點，大家喜歡你，一天接三四十次客，是很平常的，若是生意不好的話，……有時候，只有一兩個客人上門，那就只能喝西北風了。……

小文：是不是客人給我的錢，全部都要交給你？

賴：嗯，要不然，我憑什麼？化了卅五萬，買你這個人，來白給你飯吃。

賴：（暗處突有警鈴聲響起）
（警覺地，叫着）阿坤，阿坤。……

（阿坤聞聲自大門口進入上場）

阿坤：賴桑，你叫我？

賴：阿坤，剛才，警鈴響了，你沒聽見？快到後面樓上去看看，是不是有人跳樓逃走了！

阿坤：好，我這就去看。（向通內屋處下）

賴：小文，我告訴你，我這兒四處都裝有警鈴，日夜都有人看守，想逃走，門兒都沒有。……再說，你們的身分證，都鎖在我的保險箱裡，沒有身分證，即使跑了出去，也休想能找到工作，沒有人敢收留你們，……除非，你願意去坐牢。

小文：老闆娘，我一天沒吃飯了，肚子好餓，有沒有飯，先給我吃一碗。

賴：你肯聽話，……自然有飯吃。

（阿坤自內屋走出）

阿坤：賴桑，……沒有人逃走，大概是野貓碰了一下警鈴，你不用耽心。

賴：你去叫如花，出來一下。

阿坤：（向內叫）如花，出來一下，老闆娘在叫你。

（如花應聲自內屋出）

（阿坤向通大門口走出，下場）

花：老闆娘，……有客人來啊？……

一二

賴：不是有客人來，是小文她肚子餓了，你陪她去廚房，找點剩飯剩菜給她吃，順便給她洗個臉，好

花：是。

賴：你漂亮的花衣服，先借一件，給她穿，她已經答應我上班，總得打扮一下。如花，你年紀比她大，又比她先來，好好照顧她一下，說不定，一會兒，就會有客人來。她臉上的傷痕，給她搽點藥，別讓客人，看見了，倒胃口，知道嗎？

花：是，我知道。

小文：如花姐姐，……真謝謝你。

花：不用客氣，……我們走吧！

（如花領小文向內屋下）

坤：賴桑，阿福婆來了。

賴：喔！快請她進來。

坤：（向外叫）阿福婆，老闆娘，請你進來。

（阿坤自通大門口上場）

（阿福婆，打扮得很花俏的上場）

福：老闆娘，……生意好嗎？（說閩南語或臺灣國語均可）

「泣血煙花」

一三

賴：（熱情迎上）阿福婆，請坐。阿坤，給阿福婆倒茶。

阿坤：是。（倒一杯茶，送上後就去大門外下場）

福：老闆娘，我介紹給你的如花，……在這兒做的還好嗎？……替你發了不少財吧！

賴：還可以啦，……阿福婆，你今天來，是不又有新的貨色要介紹給我嘞！

福：賴桑，我有個親戚，住在烏來鄉，丈夫是個船員，為了走私，被抓進去，關了起來，他太太又半身不遂，沒法帶孩子，兩個女兒，大的十三歲，小的十一歲，長得還不賴，個子也很高大，山地姑娘，身體都很結實的，……我是好心幫人忙，做好事，……特地來問你，要不要？

賴：只有十三歲，和十一歲，太小了些吧，……至少還得白養她兩、三年，……（表示為難）……

福：你呀，吃虧的買賣，你是不會做的。對了，我聽說這年頭，客人就喜歡「老牛吃嫩草」，十五、六歲的「幼齒」，可吃香的哪，對不對？

賴：你消息倒很靈通啊！

福：她母親說了，……要是你不想要，她就打算把她們賣到酒家去，……或者，送到「歌劇院」去做「牛肉秀」。

賴：那賺不了多少錢的，……還是賣給我，比較實惠，看你的面子……我先看看「貨」，怎麼樣？

福：好呀，……當然，……要先看了貨，才好談價錢！

賴：是不是在門外，……叫她們進來吧！

福：這一陣子，我聽說外面風聲很緊，報紙上老在登有人買賣「雛妓」的消息，你空的話，我這就陪你去看一看，條子又常來華西街「臨檢」，為了怕給你惹麻煩，我要她們在附近的冰果店等著，你空的話，我這就陪你去看一看，很近的。

賴：阿福婆，你可想得真週到。

福：那，……我們現在就去吧！……

賴：好呀，……阿坤，你進來招呼生意，我和阿福婆有事出去一下，這兒就交給你了。

阿坤：賴桑，你放心，錯不了。……你儘管去好了。

賴：阿坤，等一下，我回來，若是少了一個，我就唯你是問。

阿坤：安哪，放心就是了。

（賴偕阿福婆向大門口出，下場。）

（阿坤一人在場，去到矮櫃，找出一瓶米酒，倒入杯子，喝起來，一邊打開收音機，聽起「歌仔戲」來，聲漸低弱下去。）

（壁上時鐘響了一下，顯示已過了半小時左右）

（如花手提小化裝箱，偕小文自內屋走出，小文已吃飽了肚子，洗過臉，化了裝，並穿上了花花綠綠的漂亮衣服，與前已判若二人。）

一五

［泣血煙花］

花：小文，……你爸也真是的，怎麼會欠下這麼多債呢？

小文：還不是讓「六合彩」給害的。本來，他做泥水工，做的好好地，因爲有個朋友做「六合彩」的組頭，到工地找他，要他好玩，簽一支，誰知一下子，中了十幾萬，……這樣，他就着了迷，連工也不做了，老是盯着開獎，……結果，就一直「摃龜」，再也沒有中過，……

花：哼，……很多人，都是這樣！

小文：爲了想翻本，他就越簽越多，越賭越大，房子輸掉了，還不肯罷休，最後，我就成了「犧牲品」！……被賣到這兒來。

花：你媽呢？

小文：我媽，爲了不讓爸去賭，天天吵架。前兩年，和爸鬧翻了，離婚走了。聽說，現在，她在一個酒廊上班！……

花：你有沒有去找過她？

小文：我不知道地址，只知道，她在林森北路上班，那一帶，盡是酒廊，我怎麼去問？……

花：小文，……你的命比我好，……有父親，還有母親，……我很小，父母就死了，單靠我外婆把我養大，沒有飯吃，只好去拿廟裡別人拜祭的供品來吃，……後來，我外婆也死了，爲了把她下葬，才被賣到這兒來！……

小文：（嘆了一口氣）唉，如花姐姐，我們都是可憐蟲！

（這時，阿坤已很有醉意的，站了起來，搖搖晃晃打着酒嗝的走近小文，向之打量了一番）

阿坤：嘿！……小文，你一化了裝，我都幾乎不認得你了。（拉小文的手）來，來，……坐下來陪我，好好的喝兩杯！

小文：（拒絕，掙脫手）不，……你放開我。

花：阿坤，老闆娘呢？

阿坤：有事，出去了，現在，我是這兒的「老大」，你們，都得聽我的，如花，來，先讓我親一個，叫我一聲好聽的！（如花想避開，阿坤上前將之抱住，強吻，如花躲不掉，只能忍受）……叫呀！……

花：（機械無奈地）親愛的，……阿坤哥！……

阿坤：對了，這才像話，……來，陪我喝酒。（取杯子又倒滿一杯酒，交給如花）

花：喝酒，就喝酒，來，乾杯！（一飲而盡）

阿坤：乾杯！（也乾了，又倒滿一杯酒，拿給小文喝）小文，該輪到你喝了，……你喝不喝？

小文：我不會喝！

花：小文，……你就喝了，不喝，他不會放過你的！

小文：（倔强的）我……就是不喝！

阿坤：（生氣）你不喝，你是想「敬酒不吃吃罰酒」，是不是？（猛的將酒潑在小文的臉上）你給臉

「泣血煙花」

一七

不要臉，老子可不是好惹的！……你不喝，今天晚上，我就要你，陪我睡覺，讓你知道，我阿坤的厲害！

小文：（害怕）不，……我不要。

阿坤：你不要，……我要！（上前抱住小文，強吻，並動手動腳，大吃豆腐，小文極力掙扎，逃不出魔掌）

花：阿坤，別這樣！（上前勸說拉架）小文還小，你就放過了她！

阿坤：別攔着我，……老子，高興，……你敢不肯嗎？……哈！……我非要你肯不可！

（二人正在拉扯間，小文已被抱起，向內屋走去時，小文的父親石三郎自大門口上場，他衣着襤褸，手提一包食物）

石：小文

（坤見有人進入，手一鬆，小文落地，奔向父親懷抱）

小文：爸──（哭泣着）

阿坤：（看清原來是小文的父親）哈！原來是你呀！……你把她賣都賣了，還來找她幹什麼？

石：我來看看她，不行嗎？小文，……你在這兒還好嗎？……

小文：爸，……你帶我回家，好不好？（哀求地）

石：（無言）小文，……你肚子餓不餓？……爸帶了些熱包子來，你嚐嚐。（拿包子給小文）

小文：我剛吃了飯，我不餓！

阿坤：姓石的，你的女兒，……來了，都快一個星期了，還沒上過一天班，你這做老爸的，真該好好勸勸她，到了這兒，……還想做千金小姐，成嗎？……

石：（低聲下氣）你……多照顧！……我會感激你的。

阿坤：如花，你陪他們到屋裡去談，……我懶得跟他嚕囌！

（如花引領石及小文向內屋臥室走去）

（臥室內，燈亮，堂屋燈滅，彩玉已不在屋內，石及小文坐下後，如花告辭離去）

花：小文，你們聊吧，我不陪你們了。

（花下去後，石拿包子給小文吃）

小文：爸，我不想就在這兒，……我更不樂意接客，……老闆娘，和那個流氓保鑣，都好可怕，……就像要吃人的魔鬼一樣！……他們根本就沒有把我們當人一樣的看待。

石：（內疚）小文，……對不起你。……（拭去淚水）

小文：（捲起衣袖，拉起裙子露出大腿，傷痕纍纍給父親看）爸，你看，這些都是讓那個流氓，用鞭子抽的，……要不是，今天我答應他們接客，他們還要用香煙頭，來燙我的手掌心呢！

石：（慚愧）小文，……你還是乖乖的，聽他們的，……好少受一點皮肉之苦。爸，……把你賣給他

們，也實在是不得已。

小文：不得已，……你就會說「不得已」。

石：要不是爲了還那些欠債，那些角頭弟兄，要砍了我的手，讓我變成殘廢。眞要這樣，你的弟弟、妹妹，……他們也都會餓得沒有飯吃！

石：爸，是爲了想翻本，發財，才去簽的，盼望你們，都能過好日子！

小文：誰要你去賭「六合彩」，簽什麼「特三尾」！

小文：我不要再聽你說這些廢話，你只是爲了自己，才把我賣到這兒來，你好狠心，只是爲了還債，就不顧女兒的死活，……（怨憤地）我恨你，……我才不吃你買來的包子！

（小文將包子推開）

石：（感到難過，自責）小文，……爸，眞是太自私了，只是爲了還債，……害你，在這兒受這樣的苦。……

小文：爸，……你罵得對！……爸，……你給我一點車錢，好不好？……我打算，想辦法，逃出去，……到林森北路，找我媽去，……她會照顧我的！

石：你媽，早就不在林森北路陪酒了，……聽說，她已經跟了個日本人，到日本去了！

小文：眞的嗎？……我不相信。

石：小文，爸不騙你，……再說，我現在，手邊，也沒有錢，我今天來，是想，找老闆娘商量，能不

能再借我一些錢！……

小文：爸，……你不是來看我的！……（失望的）你再借錢，還想去賭「六合彩」，是不是？……你

根本一點也不關心我！（哭泣起來）

石：（安慰地）小文，別哭了，你再哭，爸爸也想哭了。……

（父女兩人相對而泣，悲哀的音樂升起，燈暗黑下去）

（堂屋的燈亮了，賴自通外大門上，阿坤急將酒瓶收起，迎上）

阿坤：賴桑，……你回來了，……生意說成了沒有？

賴：價錢沒談攏，我故意拖兩天，再說！

阿坤：小文的老爸來了。

賴：對了，阿坤，剛才，三七仔告訴我說，高警員馬上就要來「臨檢」，你要小文、彩玉，她們先避

一避，別給發現，小文他爸，……也叫他快走，別來惹什麼麻煩！

阿坤：是，我這就去。（向通內屋處下場）

賴：（拿出一根香煙點火吸了兩口，在盤算着）十三歲就要我出廿萬，未免太唷人了！……

（石三郎自內屋出）

石：老闆娘，你好。……我今天來，是想找你商量一件事！……我想……想……再找你……

賴：什麼事？有話快說，……

石‥‥你能不能再借我一點錢！‥‥‥我想去翻本！‥‥‥

賴‥‥免了，‥‥‥你快走吧，一會兒管區警員就要來這兒「臨檢」，‥‥‥你在這兒，礙手礙腳，‥‥‥還

是避開，走遠一點的好！

（說着，推石出去）

石‥‥好，‥‥‥我走，‥‥‥改天，我再來。‥‥‥（下場）

（電話鈴響，賴去接聽）

賴‥‥喂，‥‥‥我就是賴桑，潤嘴，你說什麼？有兩個外國觀光客人，要找兩個「幼齒」過夜，一個人

八千塊。‥‥‥好，‥‥‥要過了晚上十二點，才能去啊！什麼？要現在就去，那，

錢要「加倍」！‥‥‥不然就免談。（等了一會兒，對方同意了）什麼？加倍就加倍，OK，一句

話，什麼旅社？黛安娜賓館，五二〇房間，好，我馬上，就派人送過去，‥‥‥放心，一定包客人

滿意！（掛上電話）

賴‥‥阿坤！

（阿坤聞聲自內屋出）

賴‥‥阿坤！

阿坤‥‥賴桑，放心，‥‥‥人都藏好了。

賴‥‥阿坤，剛才，潤嘴打電話來要人，‥‥‥你帶咪咪、小麗，從後門出去，‥‥‥黛安娜賓館，五二〇

房間！‥‥‥

二二

阿坤：現在就走。

賴：嗯。

（阿坤向通後門下場）

（高警員穿警察制服，拿着一本簿子，自通大門口上場）

賴：（連忙笑臉迎上）唷，高警員，怎麼？今兒又「臨檢」啊？請坐，……來，先抽支煙，我給你倒茶。（說完敬煙，高不接）

高：我不抽煙。

賴：（急去倒茶送上）煙不抽，茶總可以喝一杯吧！……

高：賴桑，……今兒日報上，登了一封少女的「求救信」，說她被關在你這兒，已經一個星期了，她名字叫許彩玉，……是不是藏在你這兒？你老實說。……

高：賴桑，真人面前不說假話，許彩玉，真的不在你這裡？……

賴：你不相信，我的話，可以進去搜啊！

高：高警員，……我這兒的小姐，都領有牌照的，你不相信，可以親自進屋去核對照片！

賴：賴桑，……我告訴你，強逼未成年的少女，去賣淫做雛妓，這是不人道的事，也是違法的，你知道嗎？……查到，可是要吃官司的喲！……

高：好啦，……這些，我都清楚啦，……高警員，既然，你來了，……我這兒表示一點心意，請你收

下。（賴開抽屜，拿出一疊鈔票，裝入一信封送上）

高…我是奉命行事，……別來這一套，讓我進去。

（高昂首進入內屋去搜查。）

賴…嘿，不收白不收，……想找到我的把柄，門兒都沒有！

（這時，黑皮很風光的自大門外進入，上場）

黑皮…（親暱的，走近賴）嗨，老闆娘，……還記得我是誰嗎？……（走近賴，用手捏她的臉，顯示兩人關係不平常）兩個月不見，你可越來越年靑了。……

賴…（高興又嬌嗔地）死鬼，……這兩個月都不見你人影，我還以為你去死了呢！

黑皮…噓！少講這些不吉利的話，來，來，……告訴你，……我跟我們老闆，去了一趟大陸，……唔，……這是我從大陸買來送你的小禮物，……（取出一隻玉鐲為之戴上）怎麼樣，喜不喜歡？

賴…（仔細端詳玉鐲）嗯，……這還差不多，……不過，這玉鐲是真的，還是假的？

黑皮…老闆娘，拜託，我黑皮是買假貨的人嗎？……

賴…高警員在裡面「臨檢」，等他走了，……咱們出去吃宵夜，怎麼樣？

黑皮…好啊，……好久沒來了，今晚，我還打算在這兒過夜呢？……你歡不歡迎？……（向之毛手毛腳起來）

賴…瞧你這死相，……別光天化日的這樣毛手毛腳！……我不喜歡這一套！……

黑皮：好，……我現在聽你的。……到了晚上，可要聽我的唷！……

賴：黑皮，你大陸去了那些地方，說來聽聽。

黑皮：上海、廣州、福州、北京，……我都去過了，大陸上，物價真便宜得不得了，「臺胞」真神氣，到處受歡迎，……這年頭，真是一切向「錢」看，有了錢，……到那兒，都吃得開。……

賴：嘿，……難怪你去了大陸，就不想回來了！……跟多少女人在那兒風流了。你老實說！

黑皮：你何必吃醋，也不過是臨時玩玩而已，有什麼好說的！……

（高警員自內屋走出）

賴：不再坐一會兒？……

高：嗯，……你沒騙我！

賴：高警員，……怎麼樣？我沒有騙你吧？……

黑皮：高警員，你大陸去了那些地方，說來聽聽。

高：我還要到別地方去，不坐了。

（高向外走出，下場）

黑皮：（見高走後，一把摟住賴說）小賴，……有一筆好買賣，你要不要做？……包你發大財唷！

賴：什麼好買賣？

黑皮：這一次我去大陸，可找到了一條好門路！

賴：什麼好門路？

「泣血煙花」

黑皮：有人可以用漁船，走私，把「大陸妹」，帶到臺灣來，……一個人，大概，十萬臺幣，就可以

成交了，……這些「大陸妹」，不識一個字，又沒有親人在臺灣，……你買來了，愛怎麼擺佈，

就怎麼擺佈，……她們看在錢的份上，決不會逃走，或者給你找麻煩，這不是包你發大財！

賴：黑皮，你真有這樣的門路嗎？……這幾天，有些客人就問我，有沒有「大陸妹」，他們都想嘗個

新鮮，換換口味呢！

黑皮：這麼說，真把「大陸妹」弄來了，……你這兒，馬上「門庭若市」嘍！……

賴：黑皮，你別說了不做，……這件事，我就全拜託你了。……

黑皮：小賴，弄成了，我有多少介紹費好拿？

賴：這還用你說，……好處，少不了你的！

黑皮：我看，再過一兩年，……你可真要買高樓大廈了！

（兩人打情罵俏一陣，如花突匆匆自內跑出。）

花：老闆娘，……不好了。

賴：如花，發生了什麼事？

花：彩玉她跳樓逃走了。

賴：什麼？她逃走了？……阿坤，這王八蛋，……怎麼，可以讓她跑了呢？……

黑皮：別緊張，……逃不遠的，……我們想法子，去把她追回來！

賴：對，……去追回來！

（幕急下）

第二幕

時：距第一幕一個多月以後

景：同第一幕

人：賴桑、巧妹、邱阿坤、小文、如花、姚老師、石三郎、阿福婆、黑皮、小毛、許彩玉、高警員

幕啓時：

賴桑和黑皮兩人在堂屋喝酒、吃菜、慶賀合作成功。

黑皮：小賴，……來，爲了慶賀我們這一次買賣合作的順利、成功，我們來乾一杯！（倒酒

賴：好，……乾杯！（舉杯碰杯一飲而盡）

黑皮：小賴，……我黑皮說的話，可沒亂吹牛吧！……我說，可以給你找到門路，弄幾個「大陸妹」

過來，你看，還不滿一個月，就給你兌現了！……這兩棵「搖錢樹」來了，可有你錢好賺的哮！

賴：黑皮，……我有點疣心，若是給警察查到了，……我們這樣販賣人口，算不算犯法？……

黑皮：你放心，……眞要是給查到了，……我找人去疏通一下，就沒事了！……祇多罰幾個小錢，就

「泣血煙花」

擺平了。來，吃菜，……喝酒，（一邊吃，一邊喝）告訴你，小賴，天塌下來，有我黑皮，給你

頂着，你還有什麼好害怕的呢！

賴：對了，黑皮，……你帶她們來的時候，騙她們說，是做工來的，若是弄清楚，幹的這項買賣，她

　　們會不會逃走，或是自殺什麼的，給我惹麻煩？

黑皮：放心，我早就給你想好了，先不急着要她們上班，找人帶她們去吃喝玩樂，好好玩幾天，化幾

　　個小錢，給她們燙個頭髮，買幾件新衣服，再給她們穿金戴銀的裝扮一番。……

賴：這，……我已經在做了！

黑皮：等她們吃飽了，喝足了，再要她們上班，到時候……只要有錢賺，……保險她們乖乖的，爲你

　　賣命。

賴：好，……我一切都聽你的！……

　　（電話鈴響，賴接聽後，交給黑皮）

賴：喂，……那位？……好，……你等一等，……黑皮，……是你的，（低聲的）好像是你們老闆打

　　來的。

黑皮：（接聽電話，表情嚴肅）是，……老闆，我是黑皮，……什麼？……明天，……有一批貨，要

　　來，……好，……我知道了，我現在就去聯絡。……（掛上電話）

賴：怎麼？……有事現在要走啊？……

黑皮：老闆，要我馬上去辦事，……小賴，……我得走了！……

賴：晚上，……你來不來？……

黑皮：再說吧，……不來的話，我會先打電話給你。

賴：是不是，又有「人」要來？……有好的，……我還要！……

黑皮：不是「人」，……是「這個」！（用手勢比劃手槍的樣子）……

賴：槍？……

黑皮：對了，……這可也是好買賣唷！……好了，……別隨便和人說，……走漏了風聲，……就麻煩了。

賴：放心，……我不會隨便和別人說的！

黑皮：我走了，……來，再乾一杯。

（黑皮親熱的與賴乾一杯後，才匆匆離去）

（賴去把收音機打開，播出「雨夜花」的歌聲，她一人邊吃邊聽）

（稍頃，巧妹與小毛兩個年輕的「大陸妹」，自內屋出，二人身穿花綠洋裝，喜形於色）

賴：（見二人出，停止吃喝）巧妹、小毛，……你們都吃飽了嗎？

巧：吃飽了。

小毛：（也點頭）……

賴：你們穿的花衣服，還合身嗎？喜不喜歡？

巧：喜歡。

小毛：（又點頭）

賴：誰替你們化的粧，化得很漂亮。……

小毛：是莉莉。……我過去，……從來沒用過什麼化粧品。……

賴：你們到臺灣來，很不容易，……我決不能虧待你們，……你們覺得住在我這兒，好不好？……

小毛：好。……

賴：高不高興？……

巧：高興，……爲了到臺灣來，我好幾個晚上，都沒睡着覺！……

賴：我聽雷先生說，你們都不識字，是眞的嗎？

巧：是眞的。

賴：自己的名字，會不會寫？

小毛：我只會寫「小毛」，……她，……不會。

賴：噢，……你們在臺灣，有沒有親友？……告訴我！……（僞裝）我可以替你們去找！

巧：我沒有。

小毛：我也沒有。……

賴：不要騙我唷！

巧：我從來不會亂說的！

賴：我……也不會騙人的。……老闆娘，我們幾時可以上工，……一個月，究竟有多少工資？……

小毛：別急，我派人，先陪你們，好好多玩兩天，不忙着上工，……至於工錢，我決不會虧待你們，至

巧：少，可以比你們在大陸多上十倍。

巧：（訝異地）真的啊！

賴：當然，是真的，……你們在大陸，沒聽說，臺灣的工錢，要比大陸的多好幾倍嗎？

小毛：我聽人說過，不過，……我不太敢相信！……

巧：（高興地）這下子，可好了，小毛，我們可以過好日子了！……

賴：（按桌上警鈴，鈴響，阿坤自通大門處上）阿坤。

坤：老闆娘，……你有事找我？

賴：嗯！……阿坤，你現在沒事吧？

坤：沒事。……

賴：（開皮包拿出一千元錢給坤）喏，……你拿一千塊錢去，……給她們倆個去逛逛街，順便給她們買些戒指、項鍊、別針什麼的，好好打扮打扮，……所謂：「佛要金裝，人要衣裝」，……既然到了臺灣，總得給他們開開眼界，……錢夠的話，找一家卡拉OK，讓她們去，好好的玩一玩！

「泣血煙花」

坤：老闆娘，……這，錢，怕不夠吧！……

賴：（又給一千塊）那就再拿一千塊去，……（向巧，小毛說）……這可是我借給你們的，……等你們上工以後，要扣還給我的唷！……

巧：是。……

小毛：謝謝，老闆娘。

賴：她們不認識路，阿坤，你可別把她們弄丟了！……

坤：賴桑，……放心，……人在我阿坤手上，丟不了。……

賴：好，……那就一起去吧！

巧：是。……

小毛：是。

（阿坤帶巧，及小毛出，下場）

（稍頃，如花借小文，自外狼狽，衣衫不整的上，小文受了傷，一臉憔悴，痛苦萬分）

花：（走向賴）老闆娘，我們回來了。……

賴：如花，怎麼？旅館去了這麼久，才回來呀，你衣服也撕破了，臉也腫了，你跟客人打架啦？唷，小文，你怎麼也受傷了？

花：老闆娘，……我們真倒楣，遇上了幾個流氓，他們都喝了酒，在旅館裡，差一點，命都沒有了，

賴：你看，我手上、腿上，還有小文臉上，全給他們打腫了。（說著，把傷處亮給賴看）

賴：（察看了一下，表示不信）怎麼會呢？我不信，……這是真的！（正色的）快，把錢拿出來。

小文：老闆娘，……你以為我們在騙你？……他們一共有七個人，輪流把我們按在地上強暴，我們不幹，就對我們拳打腳踢，有一個還亮出一把手鎗說，再不聽話，就乾脆斃了我們！

賴：嗄，……居然敢這樣無法無天，有一個還亮出一把手鎗說，再不聽話，就乾脆斃了我們！

花：老闆娘，……我……們認倒楣算了，……那個領頭的，是那個幫派的？我找他們「老大」去算賬。

，……若是我們去報了警，就白刀子進，紅刀子出，要我們好看。

賴：小文，真是這樣說的嗎？……不准騙我。

小文：老闆娘，真是這樣說的，……要不，我出去馬上會被汽車壓死！……

賴：如花，該不是，……故意在我面前演戲吧？……

花：老闆娘，你不信，搜我的身，就是了，……我若是騙了你，故意把錢藏起來，罰我死了，下十八層地獄！……

賴：（姑且信之）好，……既然，你們都這樣說，我就姑且相信你們這一次，……不再逼你們要錢，……就讓他們白玩了一次。下次，再遇到這樣的情形，馬上打電話回來。……

花：下一次，我再也不想去旅館了！……

賴：好吧，以後，……我要阿坤，負責接送你們出去，好了，休息去吧！……

「泣血煙花」

花：是，老闆娘。……（欲下，忽又被叫住）

賴：等一下，如花，那個逃走又被抓回來的許彩玉，已經給我在黑屋子裡關了三天了，大概餓得也差不多了，……你先去弄點東西給她吃，別眞餓死了，那我就虧老本了。……好好勸勸她，還是乖乖的聽話要緊。……到了這兒，逃不掉的，跟我鬥，……她不會有好日子過的！

花：老闆娘，……你還是別再逼她了，逼急了，我想她，……也許腦筋轉不過來，眞的會去自殺！……

賴：我才不相信，她會去死呢？……小文，……你進去告訴她，……我還有更狠的花招，沒有施出來呢！……就算她是一塊鋼，我也有辦法，把它弄軟下來，何況她是肉做的人！……

小文：（被嚇得呆住了）……

花：小文，……別發楞了，我們走吧！（這時，小文見石三郎，自通外大門上）

石：小文，……你怎麼啦？一臉的傷痕，……是誰欺侮你了？把你打成這個樣子！（石安撫小文，小文混身傷痛，使石疚愧萬分）

小文：（看見父，如獲救星的衝上前去）爸，……你來了，……快救我離開這兒，……我……受不了！……再也就不下去了。

賴：石三郎，這可不是我打的，……是她自己不小心，……在外面遇上了流氓！……給白玩了！

石：孩子，……怎麼會這麼不小心呢？……

賴：如花，……你先進去。

花：是。（入內屋，下）

賴：石三郎，……你難得來，有話，到小文房裡去談，……我這兒，要做生意！……

石：老闆娘，……我今天來，……是專誠來找你的。

賴：找我？……不是來看你女兒的？……有什麼事嗎？

石：小文，……你先進去，我跟老闆娘，講幾句話。

小文：爸，……你是不是要帶我回家去？

石：小文，……你別問，……先到房裡去，……等一下，，我再告訴你。

小文：好，爸，……再見。（入內屋，下）

賴：怎麼？……你還在玩「六合彩」？……

石：老闆娘，我今天來，是想找你商量，可不可以，再借我廿萬，……讓我去翻一次本！

石：我不相信，永遠是「輸家」，……總會有中簽的一天。老闆娘，昨兒晚上，我做了一個夢，……夢見三口棺材，……這不擺明我要發財了嗎？三口棺材，……還有二隻鳥，這不是神明告訴我的「明牌」嗎？……這一回，「三二」，我非中簽不可。

賴：石三郎，……要是不中，這廿萬，你拿什麼來還我？……

石：老闆娘，……小文不是賣了給你五年嗎？……我想，可不可以讓她再延長做三年？

賴：廿萬，再賣三年，……你當然無所謂，小文，她願意嗎？

石‥她是個乖女兒，……我想，她會願意的！

賴‥石三郎，……別賭昏了頭，……你還是醒醒吧！

石‥老闆娘，你做好事，無論如何，要幫我這一次忙，我一定會中簽的，中了簽，我算五分利，馬上
　　還給你，怎麼樣，……你決不會吃虧的！何況小文，又在你的手上。

賴‥我沒有開「臺灣銀行」，廿萬，你還是另找別人去商量吧！

石‥老闆娘，你再給我一次機會，……我現在，所有的希望，都寄託在這廿萬上，要是再「不中簽」
　　，就只有「死路一條」了！

賴‥石三郎，……除了小文，你不是還有兩個女兒，一個兒子嗎？……他們多大？

石‥二女兒，今年十四歲，老三，今年十歲，兒子最小，只有七歲。……

賴‥這樣吧，拿你的二女兒來賣，廿萬，……我可以把錢先借給你。

石‥我的二女兒，她還小，……還沒有發育！

賴‥十四歲，也差不多了，……我給她多打幾針「荷爾蒙」，就成了，……有些客人，就喜歡這調調
　　兒呢！……怎麼樣？……你捨不捨得？

石‥我……怕……別人背後會說我，太……太……太不人道了！……

賴‥嘿，……你還怕人說閒話！（乾笑）哈……

石‥（猶豫着）……

賴：你不願意？……我也絕不勉強！……你還是走吧，別站在這兒，妨碍我做生意！……

石：（考慮了一陣，下決心）好吧，老闆娘……你把錢拿來，……我這就給你寫字據！……

賴：我可以開支票給你，……只是，……你別又後悔喲！……

石：（仍矛盾掙扎着，決然）我絕……不後悔，……我一定會中簽，把錢還給你的！……（小文自內屋奔出）

小文：爸，……你絕不能再賭了，……你賣了我，……難道，還不夠嗎？小梅，……她決不能跟我一樣，也賣到這兒來，受這樣的罪了，……爸，我求你……你放過了她吧！……（說得聲淚俱下）

石：小文，……你……都聽見了？……

小文：爸，……你走吧，……你真要這樣做，……我這輩子，再也不認你做爸爸！小梅，……她也會怨恨你一輩子的！……

石：（似醒悟了過來）小文，……爸……是給鬼迷住了！……你要原諒爸！……

小文：爸，一錯不能再錯，……弟弟、妹妹，……都等你回去，……燒飯給他們吃呢？……你還是快回家去吧！……（強推父出）

石：好，……好……我回家去！……（石出，下場）

（小文送走父親後，獨自回內屋下）

（賴收拾酒杯，不再吃喝，這時，突有一姚老師，自通大門外進入）

姚：請問，……這兒是十六巷四十四號吧？

賴：（用眼色打量對方）你找誰？

姚：你是？……

賴：我是這兒的老闆娘！……我姓賴。

姚：我想找一位叫許彩玉的女孩，……她是不是在這兒？

賴：許彩玉？……這兒沒有這個人，……，你一定找錯地方了！……

姚：老闆娘，我姓姚，我是許彩玉補校的老師，彩玉和我是同鄉，都是澎湖人，她的家境不好，父親已經過世，靠着母親賣菜生活，她是家裡的老大，爲了求上進，就獨自到臺北來半工半讀，……她母親認識我，就託我照顧她，……我給她在電子工廠找了一份工作，白天上班，晚上讀書，她很用功，考試都是前三名，誰知道，……上個月，突然不見了，後來，我才知道，她交了個男朋友，是個不良少年，不但騙了她的感情，而且，還把她賣到這兒來。……

賴：你在胡說些什麼？你有什麼憑證，說許彩玉在我這兒。

姚：上兩個星期，學校正忙着考試，我突然接到她寫的一封求救信，信上寫的就是這兒的地址，喏，你看，（取出信給賴看）這不會錯吧！

賴：（看信後說）這是很久以前的事了，當時，你怎麼不來呢？

姚：當時，我因爲忙着考試，實在走不開！

賴：你現在來，……遲了，……許彩玉，……她已經逃走了，……連我要找她，都找不到了。

姚：什麼？你說，她逃走了！

賴：對，……八成逃到什麼「婦女救援基金會」去了。姚老師，我看……你要找她的話，還是到「婦女救援基金會」去找，……她們，是專門收容那些逃家出走的女孩子的，一定在她們那兒。

姚：眞的，不在你這兒？

賴：姚老師，……我在她身上化了四十萬，……若是你能找到她，……要她先來還清了我這筆債！不然，……我才不會輕易放過她！……

姚：（訝然）哦，……那我去婦女救援基金會找找看！……（出，下場）

（阿福婆又換了一套體面服裝，自通外面門上）

賴：阿福婆，……你眞是越來越年輕了，今天，是什麼風？把你吹來了呀！……

福：老闆娘，……我聽說，你最近又買進了兩棵「搖錢樹」，……特地來看一看呀？……

賴：那兒有什麼搖錢樹？……我呀，……儘碰上的是「賠錢樹」。

福：這是什麼話？……從來沒聽說過，有什麼「賠錢樹」來着。

福：我化錢買來的人，逃走了，不成了「賠錢樹」嗎？……

福：老闆娘，別在我面前，睜眼說瞎話，……前兩天，我聽阿坤說，……那隻飛走了的鳥，不又被抓

「泣血煙花」

三九

回籠子來了嗎？……

賴：阿坤眞是多嘴，……什麼事，都跟你說。……阿福婆，……人是被我抓回來了，沒錯，……可是，這個爛貨，實在是讓我頭痛，她軟硬不吃，……我眞不知該怎麼治她！

福：嘎，……居然，你也遇上了「對手」！……

賴：並不是我眞的治不了她，……我是怕，逼急了，她會去尋死，，眞要是「死」了，我就賠錢，賠「大」了。

福：老闆娘，……我有辦法來對付她，……要不要我來插手，幫你這個忙？

賴：你有什麼法子來治她？

福：幹這一行，……我的資格，可比你老多了！……

賴：好，……你能治得了她，……我一定好好的謝謝你。

福：不用你拿錢來謝我，……幫我一點忙，就成了。

賴：什麼忙？你說呀！

福：我最近想再開業，也需要「大陸妹」，……你介紹兩個給我，……有「財」，大家發嗎？

賴：你怎麼知道，我有「大陸妹」？

福：這種事情，你瞞得了派出所，可瞞不了我阿福婆啊！

賴：好，……算你消息靈通，……改天，我再有「大陸妹」送來，……一定負責介紹兩個給你。

福……你可要說話算話啊！……

賴……我姓賴的說話，絕不「賴」，成了吧！……

福……痛快。……你託我的那件事，今天晚上，就包在我身上。

賴……好，……一言為定，全看你的囉！

（堂屋燈黑，暗轉）

（稍頃，臥室的燈亮）

（如花，小文在臥室裡，如花經過一陣嘔吐後，仍有噁心欲吐的情勢，小文為之撫摩背部）

小文……如花姐，……你是不是病了？要不要我陪你去看醫生去，你看你，吐得臉都白了。

花……小文，不要緊，吐了，就好過多了。

小文……我看你，已經不是一次了，老吐，是不是吃了髒東西了！

花……小文，我跟你說，我這不是病，是懷孕了！

小文……（驚喜）什麼？你懷孕了？……

花……嗯，我已經有兩個月，沒來月經了，……一定是懷孕了！小文，這件事，你千萬不要告訴老闆娘，我不想讓她知道。……

小文……為什麼不要讓老闆娘知道呢？……生小孩，不也很好嗎？

花……小文，你不知道，老闆娘，才不希望我們生小孩呢，大個肚子，怎麼能接客，客人也不喜歡呀，

「泣血煙花」

那不就不能賺錢了嗎？

小文：噢，原來是這樣，不過，你的肚子一天天大起來，遲早，她總會知道的呀！……

花：小文，……我想瞞過三個月後，才讓她知道，那時候，不方便再墮胎，她就不得不同意我把孩子生下來。……不管是男是女，我一定要好好的把他生下來。……

小文：是添丁的，你是說，那個常來找你的那個年青人的？

花：對了，他愛我，我也愛他，他答應服完了兵役，就正式來娶我，和我去法院公證結婚！

小文：如花姐，……他父母會同意他和你結婚嗎？……

花：他說，只要我懷了他的孩子，他的父母，一定會答應他和我結婚的，他說，他家在南部，有很多田地，最近賺了不少錢，拿錢來替我贖身，是不成問題的！

小文：如花姐，我真為你高興，你很快就可以跳出「火坑」，過好日子了！

花：小文，記住，千萬，別讓老闆娘知道呵！

小文：好，我答應，替你保守這個秘密。……希望，有一天，讓我也跟你一樣，就好了。……

（正談說間，忽聞敲門聲）

賴：如花，小文，快出來，生意上門了，快出來見客。

（二人應聲，起立）

花：知道了，馬上就來。

（花開門，與小文走出臥室。）

（堂屋的燈未亮，臥室的燈依然亮着，稍頃，阿福婆扶着許彩玉自外進入，彩玉臉上有血痕，已

被折磨得不像一個人了）

福：（扶彩玉進入後，彩玉自黑屋子走出，拿手搗住眼睛，怕見光線）彩玉，……你們老闆娘也眞是

太狠了，怎麼可以把你折磨成這個樣子！這手上，腿上都是用鞭子抽的，啊呀，都腫了發炎，痛

不痛？（要把她扶坐正，碰到彩玉的手膀，即叫起痛來）……

王：別碰我！

福：（輕輕的捲起玉的衣袖看到傷痕纍纍）啊，……孩子，別怕，我不會打你的，眞太可憐了，我是

來給你擦藥膏，不然會爛的！（阿福婆開門走出去，停了一下，拿來藥膏和一碗參湯，先放下參

湯，拿藥膏來爲彩玉搽傷處）你忍着點，這藥膏很靈的，消炎又殺菌，搽了很快，就可以好的。

（邊說邊搽）你眞是吃了不少苦頭了。

玉：（待手上、腿上傷處多搽過後，才說）阿婆，……謝謝你。

福：不用謝，……我只是把你當我女兒一樣看待，阿婆，……我聽說，你已經三天沒有吃一點東西，肚子一

定很餓了吧？……來，……我特地燉了一碗參湯，你趁熱喝了下去，好補補元氣。……（拿碗要

彩玉喝）

玉：阿婆，……（沒有喝）你爲什麼要對我這麼好？是不是，老闆娘要你來勸我的！……勸我去上班

「泣血煙花」

四三

，接客，對不對？……

福：彩玉，……你怎麼會這麼想呢？……

玉：我是被騙了賣到這兒來的，……我不會去接什麼客的，要她放了我，饒了我，……我會感謝她一

輩子，……若是硬逼我去做這種不要臉的事，……我馬上就去死，……我做鬼也不會放過她的！

福：彩玉，……我有個女兒，七歲的時候，生病死了，要是不死的話，……現在跟你一樣大，……我

是喜歡你，……才好心來看你，……要是你肯聽我的話，……先喝了這碗參湯，……我去跟老闆

娘說，把你贖出來，做我的女兒，好不好？……（又勸喝參湯）

玉：（訝異地）阿婆你肯贖我出去？……老闆娘說，她是化了四十萬，才把我買來的，……你肯為我

，化四十萬？……

福：你若是肯做我的女兒，叫我一聲媽，……這又有什麼划不來的呢？彩玉，……乖女兒，……這參

湯涼了，就不好喝了，還是趁熱把它喝了吧！（再度把參湯送到彩玉嘴邊）

玉：好，……我喝！（正要喝，又停住）阿婆，……你家住那兒？……家裡還有什麼人？……

福：我……住在板橋，家裡，除了我先生，就沒有別的人了，……你去的話，……我們老倆口，就不

會無聊寂寞了。……你也可以繼續去上學讀書，……我們可以替你繳學費，一直讓你讀到大學畢

業！……

玉：阿婆，你和我講的，都是真的嗎？……你不會是在騙我吧！……我已經上了別人的當，不能再受

騙了！……

福：彩玉，我相信你是個好孩子，……也是個聽話的孩子。乖，聽話，……先把這碗參湯喝了，我再去弄點飯菜給你吃，……人不吃飯，真的會餓死的，這可不是好鬧着玩的！……（再把碗送上來，喝吧！

玉：阿婆，好，我聽你的，我喝！……（接過碗，一口一口喝了下去）

福：對，這才是我的好女兒！……你先休息一下，我去給你弄飯菜來吃！

玉：阿婆，……這參湯苦苦的，……我……怎麼突然……頭暈起來，……阿婆，……你是不是？在這裡面，放了「迷魂藥」？……

福：別瞎疑心，我怎麼會這樣來對你呢？……大概是你餓久了，……才會頭暈。我……這就給你去拿飯菜來吃！……你安心等着啊！……

玉：（藥性發作）阿婆……阿婆……啊……我……

（彩玉終於不支，倒了下去）

福：彩玉，……（上前搖其身體）……你醒一醒，……你怎麼啦？……

玉：（已不省人事）……

福：（得意的笑了）嘿……嘿……（拍拍手）……

（賴聞拍手聲，拉開紙門進入臥室）

「泣血煙花」

四五

福：老闆娘，……還是我行吧！……現在，……你打她，她也不會醒過來，反抗你了。你呀，去把阿

坤叫來，……把她衣服脫光，兩個人在一起，讓你拍一套活春宮照片，等她醒了，拿給她看，…

…你還怕她，……不肯答應，乖乖地，替你做生意嗎？……

賴：阿福婆，……真有你的，……只是，她醒了，還是不肯呢？

福：照片在你手上，她會不肯？她不肯，你就把照片翻印了拿到大街上去賣，再不就寄給她家裡的人

看，……你看她肯不肯？……

賴：嗯！……這一招厲害，她非肯不可。……

福：怎麼樣？……你答應我的事，「賴」不掉了吧！

（臥室燈黑）

（堂屋燈亮，賴桑一人在場，打着算盤算賬）

（稍頃，電話鈴響，賴接聽）

賴：喂，那位，……（忽神情嚴肅起來）大哥，是你呀。失敬，有什麼吩咐？……你現在需要錢用，

要我這個月的「規費」，提早付，……好，我叫人馬上送到。……什麼？你現在人在北投杏花閣

，……有幾個新加坡來的朋友，一起喝酒吃飯，……要新來的那兩個大陸妹，去陪大家喝酒、過

夜，……大哥，你吩咐的事，還不是一句話，好，……等一下，……我要阿坤，送她們過去，…

…大概，不到半小時，就可以到，……好，再見。……

（賴說完掛上電話）

賴：（向內屋叫）阿坤！……阿坤。……

（阿坤，自內走出，邊走邊扣衣服扣子）

阿坤：賴桑，你找我？……

賴：大哥，剛才打電話來，……他在北投杏花閣請幾個新加坡來的朋友吃飯，要大陸妹去陪酒、過夜，……你現在就護送她們過去，地點在老地方，你知道啦！

坤：是，……我這就去。

賴：等一下，（打開小抽屜，拿出一疊鈔票，交給阿坤）唔，這兒是五萬塊錢，是這個月的「規費」，你也順便帶去，當面交給大哥，要他在這本子上簽個字，（交一帳簿形的小本子給阿坤）表示收到，……知道嗎？

坤：賴桑，放心，……我會給你辦妥的啦！……

賴：走之前，先跟那兩個大陸妹，說清楚，別到了現場，彆彆扭扭，讓大哥不高興，知道嗎？……

坤：是，……我會和她們說的！……

賴：好，……那你就走吧！……等一下，要巧妹、小毛，她們化好了粧，再出發。

坤：是，……我這就去通知她們。……（欲入內，忽又折回）……賴桑，……有件事，……不知，你知不知道？

四七

「泣血煙花」

賴：什麼事？

坤：（湊上去，與之耳語一番）……

賴：（訝異）噢！……有這樣的事，你怎麼知道？……

坤：是客人跟我說的！

賴：你……馬上去叫如花出來！……

坤：等我走了，你再和她說吧！

賴：（斷然）不，現在就去叫她出來。

坤：（遲疑一下）如花，……（入內屋）老闆娘叫你。……

（如花未上場前，賴去矮櫃，打開抽屜，找出一瓶藥丸來，如花才上）

賴：如花。

花：老闆娘，你找我，有什麼事？……

賴：我聽說，……你有喜了，是不是真的？……（阿坤已下場）

花：（緊張的否認）不，……沒有？

賴：（怒摑其一耳光）你還敢說沒有？還睜着眼睛和我說瞎話，……客人都告訴我了，……你還嘴硬，不想承認！

花：我只是……好久沒有「來」了，……也不一定……是「害喜」啊！

賴：過來，……讓我摸摸肚子看！

（花膽怯的上前，賴摸如花的肚子，摸了一陣）

賴：你老實說，究竟幾個月了？……

花：（知賴不掉，只能承認）快三個多月了！……

賴：不管三個多月，或四個多月，這瓶藥丸，你給我拿去，分三天把它吃下去，……聽見沒有？（交藥瓶給花）

花：老闆娘，是添丁的孩子，……他已經答應娶我，……要和我正式結婚，……他會拿錢來替我贖身的！

賴：（生氣）什麼？……這種不知道誰是爹的雜種，你也要留下。……

花：（接過瓶子，流淚哀求）老闆娘，我不想把孩子流掉。……

賴：老闆娘，……我一直聽你的話，……求你……答應我，……別逼我流產，好不好，我給你跪下。

花：你別做什麼「美夢」，……客人說的話，……你能認真？還是聽我的話，讓它流掉比較好！

（聲淚俱下的下跪！）

賴：（厲聲）別跟我來這一套，……我這兒，不准有大肚子的女人，……你不清楚嗎？……

花：（大哭）老闆娘，我求你……（下跪不起）我給你磕頭！

（小文自內屋衝出）

「泣血煙花」

四九

賴：小文，……我也求你！（下跪）求你答應如花姐了吧！……

賴：這不關你的事，小文，不用你來攪和，這是我這兒的規矩，說什麼也不能有孩子。起來，如花，聽見沒有？非流掉不可！

（二人依然下跪）

賴：（生氣）什麼？……你們竟敢反抗，不聽我的話！

花：你打，就是了，……老闆娘，……可憐我，……只求你這一次。

（賴去找出一根戒尺，準備來打，二人依然不爲所動）

賴：反了，反了，竟敢反抗，我的話，都不聽了！（動手拿戒尺猛打）

（打了一陣，高警員突自門外走上）

高：嗯！……賴桑，……這是怎麼回事？……

賴：（見高如獲救星）高警員，求你來救救我！……

花：（見高來，忙迎上）高警員，你來臨檢？……

賴：沒有什麼事，我在生她們的氣！太使我傷心了。……如花、小文，你們先起來，有話等一下，再說，……去通知大家，把房門打開，說是高警員「臨檢」來了。……

花：（小聲的）你不答應我的請求，……我就不起來！

賴：你真想造反了？……

（高這時發覺小文，小文起立，欲入內屋躲藏，高將之叫住）

高：等一等，你別走！……你叫什麼名字？

小文：（只好不走）我……叫小文。……

高：你今年幾歲？

小文：十一……十……八歲。

高：十八歲？……嘿！……（不相信問賴）她是在你這兒做的嗎？

賴：她是如花小學的同學，是來找如花出去看電影的，……好了，如花，……我答應你們，一起去看電影，……你們走吧！（邊說邊用眼神向如花暗示，速去）喏帶三百塊錢去，早一點回來，……

花：（故意不走）我……不想去了！（賴在一邊咬牙切齒）

高：如花，她真是你小學的同學嗎？……我看不太像吧！……（向小文）你把身分證拿出來，給我看一看！

小文：我……的身分證，……在老闆娘那兒！……

高：哼，……分明是未成年的「雛妓」，跟我來打「馬虎眼」，老闆娘，麻煩你和我，……還有你（指小文）一起去派出所走一趟！弄個清楚。

賴：走就走，……有什麼好怕的！……

五一

「泣血煙花」

小文‥（害怕）我……不去！（哭起來不走）……我不要去坐牢。

高‥不用怕！……你又沒有做錯事，你不會坐牢的，我只是要你去問個清楚！

（阿坤自內出）

坤‥賴桑，怎麼回事？

賴‥阿坤，我跟高警員，到派出所去一下，……他對小文有一點誤會，你馬上去「大哥」那兒，……要他和局長，通個電話！……

坤‥是，……我知道了！

高‥走！（高押着小文，賴同下）

（燈黑）

（幕徐徐下）

第三幕

時‥距第二幕一段時日後的一個下午

景‥同第一幕

人‥巧妹、小毛、如花、彩玉、小文、賴桑、邱阿坤、黑皮、阿福婆、姚老師、高警員

是大白天，但天色有些陰沉，有快下雨的窒悶感覺。

堂屋的燈未亮，臥室內有日光照射進來，巧妹，和小毛兩人在坐着交談。

巧：小毛，……你看，……（取出一條金鍊子炫耀着）我這條金鍊子，好漂亮喔，……你沒有吧！

毛：我有一個玉鐲，……你有沒有？（拿玉鐲給巧妹看）

巧：（看了一下）這是假的，……要真的玉，才值錢！……

毛：你沒有，就說是假的！……

巧：小毛，……真沒想到，……到這兒來工作，可以賺這麼多的錢！

毛：有什麼用，全交給老闆娘了！

巧：小毛，老闆娘說，到了月底，會分給我們的，……她說，可以分給我們兩、三千，……比我們在家鄉做工賺的錢，真多了十倍呢！

毛：巧妹，……我覺得，我們做這樣的事，很不好！……

巧：有錢賺就是了，……有什麼好不好的。

毛：要是給家鄉的人，知道，我們在臺灣，是在做妓女，……他們一定會瞧不起我們，再也擡不起頭來。……

巧：啊呀，……你想得真多，……隔這麼遠，家鄉的人，才不會知道，……要是有一天，我們回去，

毛：也只說是做工，賺來的錢，我們自己不說，誰會知道！

毛：紙包不住火，……我擔心，……總有一天，會被人知道的！

巧：你要怕，你就老是在這兒，再也別回去！

毛：對了，巧妹，……你有沒有感覺到，這兩天，……我下身老覺得有點疼的感覺，……我聽說，若是被傳染上了性病，尤其是什麼叫「愛滋病」的，就死定了，怎麼治也治不好的！

巧：你信誰說的鬼話來著，「愛滋病」是外國人才會得的，我們中國人，才不會得那種病呢？

毛：是真的嗎？

巧：當然是真的，……我騙你做什麼？

毛：可是我總覺得下身癢癢的，怪怪的！

巧：你呀，是疑心病，多用肥皂洗乾淨，不就沒有事了！……

毛：好吧，……我就聽你的話洗乾淨點！……

巧：小毛，……有個客人說，我的身材很棒，可以去做「牛肉秀」，只是脫光了衣服，給臺下的人看一看，……就可以賺很多的錢，你要不要一起去試一試！

毛：什麼。？……你想去做「牛肉秀」？老闆娘，會答應讓你去嗎？

巧：那個客人說，……他有個朋友，開了家什麼「歌劇院」，四處找人做「牛肉秀」，……一個月，可以賺一萬多，……比在這兒賺的還要多！……

毛：老闆娘，才不會答應讓你走呢！……

巧：那客人說，可以想法子，（向門外看了一下，才說）幫我偷偷溜走。……

毛：有人時時在看着，我們就是長了翅膀，也飛不了的，再說，……此地我們一個熟人也沒有，……

要是遇上了騙子，……想回也回不來了！……

巧：（想了一下）嗯，你說得也對，……我們是要好好考慮淸楚，才做決定，……要逃走，逃不掉的

……還是你想得週到。

（敲門聲：「巧妹，小毛，快出來，有客人來了。」）

巧：眞是的，還沒好好說上幾句話，又有客人來了！

毛：這裡的人，眞有錢，……好像錢永遠花不完似的！

（說着，二人整整衣服，拉開紙門，走出，下場）

（稍頃，彩玉拉如花，自外進入臥室後，關上紙門）

花：（坐下想了一下，又哭起來）老天爺，爲什麼我這麼苦命，想留個孩子也留不住。

彩玉：如花，別再難過了，……孩子既然已經流掉了，……你再哭又有什麼用呢？……

花：彩玉，……你不知道，……我好在意這個孩子，……有了他，添丁，……他就可以和我結婚了，

……我也可以跳出苦海了，……可是，現在，孩子沒有了，他還會再來娶我愛我嗎？

玉：想開一點，如花，……只要他是眞心愛你，……沒有孩子，他還是會和你結婚的！你倆年紀還輕

花：（灰心失望）不可能的，現在我們再也不可能結婚了！（又哭了）

，將來要多少個孩子都行。

玉：如花，……你別哭了，……你再哭，……我也想哭！……

花：我真不懂，老闆娘，怎麼會這麼狠心？……她自己也是個女人，為什麼，會要這樣欺負女人，……她自己不生孩子，要別人也不能生孩子，……這究竟是個什麼「世界」！

玉：這是一個不公平的世界，……也是一個人吃人的社會，……為了「錢」，人欺負人，壓迫人，做出連禽獸也不如的事，……我真恨，我為什麼……還要苟且偷生，活在這個世界上。……

花：……發生在你身上的事，我也為你感到難過，……她們居然會用這樣狠毒的手段來對付你，……（哭起來）

玉：彩玉，……真是太殘酷了。……

花：如花，你別說了，……你一說，我一天都不想再活下去了！……陷阱，到處都是害人的陷阱，一不小心，……就會掉了下去，……再也難以自拔！唉！……這樣的痛苦，我究竟要熬到那一天呢！……（哭起來）

花：彩玉，別難過，……你的求救信，我已經用限時專送替你寄出去了，你補校的姚老師，接到信後，一定會設法來救你出去的，……你被男朋友騙賣到這兒來，真是太冤枉了！……

玉：如花，你在這兒，被賣了幾年？……

花：三年，……我已經做了一年，若是添了不來贖我，還有兩年才能自由呢！

玉：你是怎麼被賣到這兒來的呢？

花：我很小的時候，父母就死了，靠我外婆把我養大，……外婆擺一個香煙攤子，收入很少，還常遭一些流氓欺侮，後來，外婆也死了，為了埋葬外婆，我被一個遠親賣到一個酒家去幫忙，那時，我才十四歲，派去廚房做粗活，到了十五歲，他們就逼我坐枱子，還脫光了衣服陪客人喝酒，我不願意，他們就用刀威脅我，說我不聽話，就當場殺了我！……我年紀小，很怕死，就只好答應他們。……我真沒有用……（哭起來）

玉：那又怎麼會被賣到華西街來呢？

花：在酒家做了兩年，我已經十七歲，酒家的老闆，有一個同居的女人，說我長得不錯，就帶我到臺北來，說是可以淘金，她先把我押在應召站，做應召女郎，專門跑飯店，應付觀光客，日本人、美國人、非洲的黑鬼，我都和他們睡過，有一次被警察查到，還在看守所被關了三天。……

玉：真沒想到，你吃的苦，比我不知多了多少倍。

花：後來，他們又送我到什麼「觀光文化城」去做「馬殺雞女郎」，為了我曾經逃跑過，沒有成功，最後，被一個流氓，賣到這兒來。……什麼色情的買賣，我都幹過了。……本來，我覺得活得這樣痛苦，不如死了算了，但是聽聽別人的遭遇，比我還慘，也就認了。誰知道，這時候，真巧，遇見了添丁，……他只比我大一歲，他是真心愛我，我才有勇氣，繼續活下去……

玉：如花，……你同情我，我更同情你，……我們都是受人踐踏的殘花敗柳，煙花女子，……也許，

「泣血煙花」

「泣血煙花」

花：我們這輩子，永遠也不會有明天了！……

花：彩玉，不要這樣悲觀，好不好？……你比我大兩個月，……我叫你做姐姐，好嗎？彩玉姐。……

玉：如花，……（擁抱如花）我的好妹妹，……我只是比你多讀了幾天書而已，我實在沒有資格，做一個保護你的好姊姊。……

花：彩玉姐，有個人可以說說心裡頭的痛苦，也比沒有人說，要好些，你說對不對？

玉：如花妹妹，你心裡的痛苦，我很瞭解，而我心裡的痛苦，不是你所能想像的！唉……（哭起來

花：姐姐，……求求你，別哭了。（也哭起來）

（二人哭作一團，燈漸暗，黑掉）

（堂屋的燈光亮了）

（賴桑一人在悠閒的嗑着瓜子，喝着茶，這時，阿福婆又換了一套衣服，自外上場）

福：老闆娘，……

賴：阿福婆，你來啦？……來，嗑瓜子，喝茶。（說着去倒了杯茶給福

福：老闆娘，……上回你答應我的事，你沒忘了吧？

賴：什麼事，你不說，我可眞記不起來了。

福：那個叫「彩玉」的，已經乖乖的「上班」了吧？……有沒有再不肯「聽話」？……

賴：阿福婆，……你幫我的這個忙，我忘不了的，……彩玉，現在，比誰都聽話，……喜歡她的客人

五八

，還真不少呐！……對了，阿福婆，我想起來了，你是說，給你介紹「大陸妹」的事，怎麼隔了這麼多天了，還沒給你「兌現」對不對？

福：對啦，我等得多望穿眼了，究竟那一天，才能來呢？

賴：阿福婆，放心，……這件事，我早就和黑皮交待過啦！這一陣子，……他忙着做別的買賣，……大概……不出十天，……他給我保證，一定可以，多帶幾個回來的，……你別心急，耐性等着就是了！……

賴：既然你這麼說，……我就放心了。……

福：黑皮跟我說，……這件事，對外……千萬要保密，絕不能，對外亂嚷嚷，……讓警察條子知道了，就麻煩了！

福：放心，……我才不會去亂嚷嚷呢！對了，老闆娘，……那個小文的爸，最近，沒再來找你借錢了吧！

賴：你是說，……那個叫石三郎的賭鬼？……自從小文被帶走了以後，就沒再見他來過？……我正想找他算帳呢？

福：找他算帳？你別找他了，他呀，……現在在裏面住「不花錢」的旅館，吃「免費」的飯菜呢！

賴：他……被關起來了？……

福：他真是賭昏了頭，為了還賭債，居然綁票別人的小孩，想發大財！……開口要兩千萬。……

「泣血煙花」

賴‥結果，財沒發成，人倒被關進去了，是嗎？……

福‥對啦！……我看這下子，至少也得坐上幾年的牢，……他在裡面是餓不死，……留下的幾個孩子，可就慘了。……

賴‥臺灣，餓不死人的，……她們可以來找我們倆討生活啊，對不？哈……

（正說着，電話鈴響，賴去接聽）

賴‥喂，……我是老闆娘，……你找誰？……如花？……她正忙着，……什麼？你有要緊的話，……和她說，……火車快要開了，……你是在火車站打的電話，……（不耐煩）好吧，我去叫她出來，……你別掛斷。……

（放下話筒，賴走向通內屋處叫着）

賴‥如花，快出來，……有你的電話。……

（阿福婆嗑完瓜子，起立）

福‥老闆娘，你忙吧，……我改天再來陪你聊天。……

賴‥好，我不送啦！

（阿福婆下場後，如花自內屋走出

賴‥長話短說，別老佔線，我這電話，是隨時有生意上門的。

花‥是，老闆娘。……（接聽電話）我是如花，……添丁，是你打來的，……你說，……什麼？……

六〇

賴：你父親不同意，你和我結婚，說我是妓女，配不上你，……說我流掉的孩子，也不一定是你的，

……你決定和我分手，……叫我不要難過，（哭起來）……我能不難過嗎？……你……走吧，……

……我再也不要見你！……（說着掛上電話，哭起來）

賴：如花，別哭了，……男人都是這樣的，你還擔心，將來沒人會娶你！……

花：老闆娘，孩子是你逼我流掉的，……現在，我什麼都沒有了，……添丁，也不肯來替我贖身了，

……難道我哭還不准我哭嗎？……

賴：（厲聲喝阻）我就是不准你哭，哭哭啼啼，又沒死人，會帶來晦氣的，……你懂不懂？快把眼淚

擦了，抹上胭脂花粉，高高興興的去接客做生意，（大聲地）聽見了沒有？

花：（強壓抑止不哭，但壓不住，低聲抽泣）……

賴：你……不聽我的話，……小心，……我等下，怎麼來收拾你。……

花：我……（忍耐）不……（哭起來）哭就是了。……

賴：（生氣）這是什麼態度！……越來越不像話！……（急奔入內屋下）

（這時，黑皮形色慌張的匆匆自外進入）

黑皮：小賴，……賴桑！……

（賴自內屋走出）

賴：怎麼？……你又好幾天，沒到這兒來了？……

黑皮：小賴，……你這兒，有沒有隱秘的地方，……可以讓我暫時躲幾天？……

賴：怎麼？發生了什麼事，是不，有人要找你的麻煩？

黑皮：我們「老大」出事了，……那些走私運進來的「黑貨」，已經被治安機關，查到扣留了，……現在人也被關了進去，要不是我機警，溜得快，……也難逃法網，……小賴，（掏出一把鎗交給賴）這把鎗，你暫時保管一下，……我……想，要是你這兒不方便躲，我只好先到南部去避避風頭了。……

賴：（拒收鎗）這鎗，……還是你自己帶着，……我這兒人進人出的，那兒藏得住人，……這樣吧，……（開抽屜拿出一疊鈔票給黑皮）我這兒，有六、七萬塊錢，你先拿去，做路費，躲過一陣再說。……

……（黑皮將鈔票收入口袋，將手鎗也放入腰間）

黑皮：小賴，……謝了，……要是不死……我會回來看你的！

賴：你多保重！

黑皮：對了，那兩個大陸妹……你最好……也別讓她們出去，……這兩天，報上已經登出消息，……條子也可能隨時找上門來，……會把她們，送回大陸去！……

賴：……噢，……是嗎？……

黑皮：我……走了，……走後門，比較安全，別送我了。

「泣血煙花」

六二

賴：好，我不送了。……

（黑皮四處張望，匆匆向通內屋下場）

（稍頃，電話鈴響，賴接聽）

賴：喂，……那裡，……你是黛安娜賓館的小沈，……我就是賴桑，……你說什麼？那個克拉克先生，今天還不走，要昨天陪她的那個小毛，再陪他一晚，……還是老價錢，……好，……等一下，我就讓小毛過去，……七〇七房，……我記住了。（掛上話筒）

（賴按電鈴，響。阿坤聞聲自外門上場）

坤：賴桑，你叫我？

賴：你去把小毛叫出來，昨天，黛安娜賓館的那個客人，還要她，再去陪他一晚，……你……叫個計程車，送她去。……

坤：好，我去通知她。……（向通內屋下，很快的，小毛隨之出。）

小毛：老闆娘，……我不去，好不好？……

賴：那個客人，很喜歡你，……你去，多賺一點錢，不好嗎？……

小毛：老闆娘，你不知道，那個人有虐待狂，又髒，又臭，不聽他的，就動手打我！……你看，……（露出腿上的傷痕），……這都是他打的！……

賴：他要你怎麼樣，你聽他的，不就好了嗎？……

「泣血煙花」

小毛：他真不要臉，……他……居然，要我用嘴去吃他的「那個」，……我不肯，……他就狠狠的打

我，昨晚還拿刀子出來，可把我嚇死了，……我這輩子再也不要看見他！

賴：（生氣）小毛，……你真的不去？

小毛：我……不去。（堅決地）說什麼也不去。

賴：（怒）你……敢不聽我的話？……告訴你，……你去也得去，不去也得去，……要不我就打得你

皮開肉裂，有你好受。

賴：阿坤，拿皮鞭子來。

坤：是。（去拿了一根皮鞭子送上）

賴：你不去，是吧，……我非打得你去！

坤：小毛！……你去了吧！……老闆娘發起火來，……你可受不了的。

小毛：要去你去！……我不去，……（大聲地）我就是不去！

小毛：（倔強地）我……就是不去，你打好了！……

賴：阿坤，把她抓住！

（賴用力打小毛，小毛閃躲，用手擋遮）

小毛：老闆娘，你改派別人去，就說我病了，不行嗎？

賴：阿坤，把她抓住！今天，我要殺雞給猴子看，就是打死她，我也認了！

（阿坤抓住小毛，賴狠狠打了幾下，忽巧妹匆匆自內屋出）

巧：老闆娘，不好了。……

賴：什麼事？……（停止抽打）

巧：那個叫許彩玉的，……在她房裡，……用一根繩子，上吊自殺死了！

賴：什麼？彩玉上吊自殺死了？……阿坤，快去，抱她下來，看還有沒有救？……

坤：是。（急入內屋下）

巧：（發現小毛被揍，關心地）小毛，你是怎麼啦？……

賴：有個外國客人，喜歡她，要她今晚再去，……她竟然不聽話，不想去！……

小毛：（哀哭）巧妹，……你不知道，……那個客人，根本就不把我們當人看待，……我長這麼大，……從來沒有這樣被人欺負過！……

巧：小毛，……還是聽老闆娘的話，……比較好！……

賴：巧妹，還是你懂事，好好勸勸她，跟我作對，……是自己跟自己過不去！……

（阿坤自內出）

坤：賴桑，……斷氣很久了，……再人工呼吸也沒用，沒有救了。……

賴：（嘆了一口氣）唉，……我真倒霉，化了四十萬，好不容易，讓她喝了阿福婆的迷魂湯，……還沒賺回個零頭，這下子，我的本錢等於丟入淡水河，全泡湯了！……

坤：賴桑，……要不要去報案？……

賴‥報什麼案？……這件事，大家不准張揚出去，讓管區警員知道了，更是麻煩。……阿坤，到了晚

上，你用麻布袋一裝，綁塊大石頭，往淡水河一丟，就了事，……你會辦嗎？

坤‥我會辦的，……只是，……我可不想白幹！

賴‥放心，……我是會讓你白幹的人嗎？……只是，口風要緊。

巧‥老闆娘，彩玉，怎麼好好的，會想自殺呢？……

賴‥誰知道，……有吃有穿，我又沒虧待她，竟然會去自殺，真是活得不耐煩了！……

（這時，高警員自外上，音效加強）

高‥賴桑，你……說誰會去自殺，活得不耐煩了！

賴‥（急掩飾）高警員，我……只是隨便和她們談談。做人免不了有許多不如意的事，怕他們想

不開，免得去自殺。

高‥老闆娘，……你這裡常來一位叫黑皮的客人，今天來過沒有？……

賴‥他，好久都沒有來了，……高警員，找他有什麼事嗎？……（發覺巧妹，小毛在場，頗爲不妥，

乃用手勢暗示她倆進去，巧妹，小毛未察覺）

高‥我有事要問他，他真的今天沒有來過？

賴‥你不信，可以去搜呀！……我騙你幹嗎？（向巧妹說）你們進去，……這兒沒有你們的事！

高‥（看出二人似大陸妹）等一等。

（巧妹，小毛未能入內，停步，高上前向二人打量了一下）

高‥你們兩位，……怎麼我從來沒見過？那兒來的？……

巧‥（緊張）！我……我……

高‥你呢？（問小毛）

小毛‥我……是外地來的！……

高‥你今年幾歲？

小毛‥我是一九七二年出生的！

高‥（察出破綻）一九七二年？……你是在大陸出生的吧！……老闆娘，……請你把她倆的身分證，拿來，我看一下。

賴‥高警員，明人不說暗話，……不錯，……她倆是偷渡來的，……你能不能高擡貴手，……放她們一馬，……這兒，又沒有外人，……（開另一抽屜，拿一疊鈔票送上）……這些，……表示一點心意，可以嗎？……

高‥老闆娘，……我……很抱歉，……這錢，你自己留着，……我不能收，……你和她們倆個，和我一起，去派出所走一趟吧！……

賴‥好，你不收錢，……我跟你去！……阿坤，……這兒，你暫且招呼一下，我很快就回來的！

巧‥我不要被送回去。

（高押着巧妹，小毛，賴桑一行，向大門外走去，下場）

小毛：我也不要被送回去！（聲漸遠）

坤：真是夜路走久了，……遲早會遇見鬼！……

（如花自內屋走出，手拿一封信）

花：阿坤，……老闆娘呢？

坤：跟高警員，還有巧妹，小毛她們，都到派出所去了。……

花：是不是為彩玉自殺的事？

坤：不，是「大陸妹」的事，……看樣子，她倆不能做了。如花你找老闆娘，有什麼事嗎？

花：沒事，只是看她在不在，剛才我睡覺的時候，發現彩玉，在我枕頭底下，留了一封遺書，……要我代她寄回到澎湖去給母親的！……

坤：彩玉還寫了遺書，這給警察知道了，又不得了，老闆娘曾關照說，彩玉自殺的這件事，要我們不要隨便說出去……

花：我看，這封遺書，……還是點火，把它燒了的好！……（欲將信拿去）

花：不，不行，怎麼可以燒掉呢！我不能這麼做，彩玉她既然托了我，我就一定得給她辦到。

坤：（拒絕將信交出）不，不行，……

花：不，……你還是給我，燒了的好，寄出去，會惹麻煩的！……

花：不行……這是彩玉，要我寄給她母親的，……我決不能給你。……

（正爭執間姚老師自外上場）

姚‥請問，‥‥‥許彩玉，‥‥‥她是不是眞的住在這兒？‥‥‥

花‥請問，你是誰？‥‥‥你找許彩玉，有什麼事嗎？‥‥‥

姚‥我是許彩玉補校讀書的姚老師，‥‥‥我最近又收到一封她寫給我的限時信，她說，她活得很痛苦，一定要我來救她出去！‥‥‥

花‥姚老師，‥‥‥你就是她補校的姚老師，‥‥‥（痛哭失聲的說）你‥‥‥來晚了一步，彩玉，她活不下去‥‥‥已經自殺‥‥‥死了，‥‥‥你再也見不到她了！‥‥‥

（强烈震撼，配音效）

姚‥什麼？彩玉，她‥‥‥自殺‥‥‥死了，‥‥‥我來晚了？‥‥‥

（將信交上）這是她留給母親的遺書，你自己看吧！

（坤欲阻止。已來不及，姚取出信紙，來看。）

花‥‥‥來不及，‥‥‥

（屋內燈光全黑，用聚光燈自頂上照下來，姚與花同在看信，信由彩玉含淚幕後唸出來）

彩玉‥（Ｏ‧Ｓ）親愛的母親‧‧‧‧原諒你不孝的女兒，‥‥‥做了這樣的傻事，希望你別難過，‥‥‥誰知道人心是這麼醜陋詭詐，我做夢也沒想到，遇上輝中這一愛情騙子，他竟然會狠心，把我賣到妓女戶來，‥‥‥爲了不肯接客，我拚命反抗過，‥‥‥但是沒有用，‥‥‥我還是向她們屈服了，‥‥‥爲了人性的尊嚴，我只好自己結束這痛苦的一生，‥‥‥媽，我沒有什麼留給你，只好留下這一束

頭髮，給你做個紀念，原諒我吧，不孝的女兒彩玉淚書。……

（遺書唸完燈復明）

花：（看完已泣不成聲）彩玉，……你為什麼要走上絕路呢？……為什麼去死呢！……

姚：唉，……彩玉，老師，沒能早一天趕來救你，……叫我怎麼去見你的母親呢？

花：姚老師，這封信，就交給你，帶回去，給她媽看吧！……

姚：彩玉，……這信和這束頭髮，我一定為你帶回家去，我會把你的故事，告訴所有的年青人，免得別人也和你一樣被騙受害，我來晚了一步，彩玉……（哭）

花：姚老師，……你領我進去讓我見她最後的一面！……

姚：（拭淚）好，……彩玉的屍體，……還在後面，……你要不要進去，看她最後的一面！

（花偕姚老師向內屋進去，下場）

坤：（坐在沙發上思想着）老闆娘，怎麼還不回來呢？……我看，……彩玉的後事，……還是請姚老師來辦吧！隨便丟到淡水河去，……總不太好！……

（燈光逐漸暗下來）

（恐怖的音樂升起，慘綠色的燈光下，彩玉披頭散髮，猶如鬼魂般出現，站立距阿坤坐的沙發前不遠處。）

彩玉：阿坤，……（用ＡＣＨＯ廻音）……

坤：（心悸萬分）彩玉，……是你自己自殺死的，……可別來，嚇我呀，……和你拍的那些照片，……

……也是老闆娘要這樣拍的，你……要報仇，……要算賬，……你要找老闆娘去，千萬別來找我！

（彩玉逐步逼進阿坤，他無法脫身，全身縮後，往沙發內擠。）

（阿坤一邊退，一邊想站起來，但腳發軟，直發抖。）

彩玉：阿坤，……我不會放過你的。……

坤：阿坤，……我不會放過你的。……

（彩玉走近阿坤，阿坤雙手抱頭不敢面視，彩玉捉住他，阿坤駭怕大叫）

坤：放開我！我的媽呀，老天爺呀，……放開我。……

（燈光暗，彩玉突然消失，賴桑換上其位置）

（在燈光尙黑時，坤不斷喊叫直到燈光再亮，彩玉鬼魂消失，在拉阿坤衣袖的原來是賴桑）

坤：（手放下抬頭看）賴桑，原來是你，……

賴：阿坤，你怎麼啦？……嚇得這個樣子！把褲子都尿濕了？

坤：（餘悸猶存）剛才，……我看見彩玉，……她的鬼魂來找我算賬！……

賴：算賬？是她自己自殺死的，……爲什麼找你算賬？……

坤：老闆娘，剛才，……我眞看見她的鬼魂來找我他，……我不騙你。

（電話鈴響，賴先不敢接聽，再響了一陣才接聽）

賴：喂，……我是賴桑，……什麼？克拉克在催問，小毛，怎麼還沒有送去賓館，……小沈，……小

毛：她被條子抓走了，……她不能去了，……克拉克他要是同意，我改派另一個小姐前去，……好，我再等你電話。……

賴：阿坤，……彩玉的屍體，你料理了嗎？

坤：還沒有。……

賴：（思索了一下）這樣吧，別丟淡水河了，通知殯儀館派人來，暫時放入冰庫，想法子通知她家人來料理。

坤：對，這樣比較好，我這就去辦。（匆匆出門下場）

（這時，小文忽又自通外門的地方上場）

賴：小文，……你……怎麼回來了？……

小文：老闆娘，……我爸，犯了法，……被關在牢裡，而我的弟弟妹妹，又太小，沒有辦法賺錢生活下去！……為了照顧她們，能有飯吃，……我想了又想，決定還是回來給你做，……你肯不肯要我，收留我？

賴：你……真的要回來跟我做？……以前，你欠的賬，……還沒還清啊？……

小文：只要你肯答應我做，……我想總有一天，欠你的賬，會給你還清的！……

賴：好吧，……可憐的孩子，……我答應你，讓你做下去。……

小文：老闆娘。……（欲言又止）……

賴：小文，你肚子餓了，是不？餓的話，自己去廚房找飯吃！

小文：謝謝老闆娘，……那我去了。（入內，下）

（燈光漸暗下去）

（這時場上，僅剩賴一人，她抽一支煙，陷入沉思中）

（恐怖音效升起，彩玉幽魂，在陰暗中再度出現，一步步向賴走來。）

賴：（駭極）彩玉，……你……你……不是死了嗎？……你……別來嚇我！……

彩玉：老闆娘，……還我命來！……（走近賴，雙手掐住賴脖子，欲置其於死地）

賴：（大叫）……啊！……

（幕急下）

（全劇終）七十九年初稿。八十一年十一月十二日三度修正。

姜龍昭舞臺劇劇本

復　　　活（獨幕劇）三十八年演出。

寶島之蠹（獨幕劇）三十九年演出。

視　察　員（獨幕劇）三十九年獲中華文藝獎金委員會獎金並演出。

烽火戀歌（歌舞劇）四十一年由總政治部出版。

榕樹下的黃昏（兒童劇）四十一年獲臺灣省教育廳徵求兒童劇首獎。

奔向自由（獨幕劇）四十二年獲總政治部軍中文藝獎獎第三名，並由總政戰部出版。

國軍進行曲（五幕劇）四十三年獲總政治部軍中文藝獎多幕劇佳作獎。

父與子（獨幕劇）五十六年獲「伯康戲劇獎」獨幕劇第四名，並由僑聯出版社出版。

孤星淚（四幕劇）五十七年獲「伯康戲劇獎」多幕劇首獎，並由僑聯出版社出版，後又改名為「長情萬縷」拍成電影。「多少思念多少淚」由遠大文化出版公司出版。曾由中央電影公司改編

紅寶石（獨幕劇）六十年中國戲劇藝術中心出版。

眼（四幕劇）六十四年獲「李聖質戲劇獎」首獎，並由商務印書館出版。

吐魯番風雲（五幕劇）六十五年獲「臺北市話劇學會」第三屆藝光獎，並由商務印書館出版。

金蘋果（兒童劇）六十七年獲教育部徵求兒童劇首獎，並由中國戲劇藝術中心出版。

國　　魂（五幕劇）七十年獲教育部徵求舞臺劇首獎，七十一年又獲總政治作戰部頒發「光華獎」，由遠大文化公司出版。

沒有舌頭的女人（四幕劇）七十一年由遠大文化公司出版。

金色的陽光（四幕劇）七十二年獲行政院文建會徵求舞臺劇首獎，七十三年並由文建會出版。

幾番漣漪幾番情（三幕劇）七十二年受文建會邀請與人聯合編寫，七十三年由文建會出版。

一隻古瓶（四幕劇）七十三年由「文學思潮」雜誌社出版。

孟母教子（四幕劇）七十三年完成，七十七年二次修正。

母親的淚（五幕劇）七十三年獲教育部徵求舞臺劇本文藝創作獎第三名，並由教育部出版。

淚水的沉思（四幕劇）七十四年完成，七十七年定稿，獲教育部徵求舞臺劇文藝創作獎佳作，並由教育部出版。八十年由文史哲出版社出版英譯單行本。

陶匠與泥土（四幕劇）七十八年完成。

飛機失事以後（三幕劇）八十年完成。八十一年由文史哲出版社出版英譯單行本。

泣血煙花（三幕劇）七十九年完成，八十一年由文史哲出版社出版英譯單行本。

雪花紅塵夢碎（五幕劇）八十一年完成。

「泣血煙花」

ANGELS IN HELL

An Original Play

by

Chiang Lung Chao

Translated into English

by

Elizabeth Chiang Moxon

John Sawyer Moxon, Editor
Rosamond A. Moxon, Editor

December, 1992

The Liberal Arts Press

P. O. Box 7-99, TAIPEI, TAIWAN
REPUBLIC OF CHINA
1992

Foreword:

The author has been involved in writing and mass media work for over four decades. During this time he has always had a full time job at one of the major networks, writing in his spare time. He has written twenty four plays, several novels, various movies, stage plays, and opera critiques. Throughout his career, he has won more than forty prizes and awards for his work. Currently he is working at China Television Company and teaching part time at colleges on Media and broadcasting.

My wife, Elizabeth, first met Mr. Chiang about thirty years ago. She was a teenager then newly selected by the Nikatzu Film Co. and had just finished her training in Tokyo, Japan. Upon her return from Japan, under contract with the Central Motion Picture Theatre Co. she hosted a talk show for Taiwan Television Co. where Mr. Chiang was in charge of program quality contral. My wife is grateful for Mr. Chiang's kindness and helpfulness for his students or new comers. In 1992, when my wife decided to go back to theater related work, she started by translating some of his work in the hope it would be produced and performed by college students. I am very proud that both of them are working hard for the benefit of education of the next generation.

It was very kind of the author of the play to ask me to express my personal feelings on the issue of under-aged prostitution. As we all know, prostitution is the oldest profession in the world. It is universal. No matter where you are, there are prostitutes usually handled by evil pimps in the shadows. In recent years there has been a phenomenon that the number of under-aged prostitutes (minors) has risen dramatically.

As I understand it, in Taiwan this has happened for several reasons. First, through the superstition that an older man will gain or maintain his youth by copulating with young girls. Secondly, that many men who are sexually inadequate derive sexual satisfaction from the domination of young girls. Thirdly, are those who got rich too quickly to handle themselves, and constantly seek different excitements.

In the past, the public in Taiwan has failed to point out and speak up about such abnormal behavior. It is clearly evil to abuse another human being in such a way. We need to educate people that

such inmoral acts are a sickness and not something of which to be proud.

In the United States, we have runaway teenagers, who will prostitute themselves for money to support a drug habit or other perceived desire. Those teenagers however, do so to survive on their own, and are not forced by their parents. In spite of much criticism of our social system, the Child Warefare Agencies do try to protect our children. We also have child pornography, but not child prostitution. When it does occur, it is prosecutable, and the child will be protected.

Taiwan, considered an outstanding member of the world community, very advanced in many ways and with a high economic profile, is to be shamed that the act of buying and selling a human being, (especially your own) into prostitution, still exists. I am sure that there are laws against such crimes, but if the Justice Department doesn't enforce them and punish the offenders severely, the laws are of no value.

In other advanced counties, to reduce under-aged prostitution, action has been taken to protect runaways and work with family counselling and drug rehabilitation programs. In Taiwan, action may be necessary on both the supply and demand. On one hand, provide a better social service program so that the needy will not have to sell their children to suvive. Severely enforce and punish those who commit such crimes, which includes buying and selling human beings as well as having sex with minors. On the other hand, educate the general population, that to have sex with a minor is not fashionable, it is a mental illness. This sickness is as abnormal as incest. Last but not least, we, the silent good majority, can no longer be silent and let this continually happen around us. Let that minority know that their inhuman acts are a reflection on all of us, and we are not going to stand for it. Condemn them, tell your representatives and your lawmakers that it is time to clean up the sickness of this society that has been caused by too rapid and unequally distributed material growth.

Time: Summer of 1989, or any time that is applicable.

Act One: June, 1989.

Act Two: July, 1989.

Act Three: Two weeks later, one afternoon in July.

Place: A Red Light district in Taipei, Taiwan. May apply to any city.

Scenery: The stage is divided into three sections. The main part of the stage is the living room of a brothel. It consists of a sofa, coffee table, end table, telephone, chairs, and any other furniture. At the back of this main room is a large bay window, through which the audience can see the day light or neon lights at night. The audience can also hear the noise of the people and cars on the street. The door to the outside is in the far right corner. At the left front of the stage, there is a small bedroom. It is furnished with a bed, dressing table, chairs, and closet. It is illustrative of the several other individual rooms for the prostitutes at the back of the building, which occupy the farthest area of the stage. At the left back stage are doors to other rooms for the customers to use. The nearest door to both the living room and the left front bedroom is where the beating takes place.

Characters:

Ann: A fifteen year old girl. She was sold into prostitution by her own father, under the pressure of gangsters, in order to help pay his gambling debts.

Jade: Eighteen years old. She was betrayed and abducted by her boyfriend. He sold her for a sum of money to the brothel, in which she is forced to do illegal prostitution. She suffered physical brutality for refusing to cooperate. She was tricked, drugged and blackmailed into losing her virginity. She gave up her life in order to gain her dignity.

Rose: Around eighteen years old. She was born in poverty and was forced to sell her body at a young age in order to pay for her

3

grandmother's funeral. She has worked at many different prostitution establishments.

Sue: A woman in her late forties. She is the owner of a brothel. She uses her connections with the mob to run her business illegally. It includes abduction and unlicensed or under age prostitution, etc.

Clint: A young muscle man in his twenties. He works as a bouncer and bodyguard. He carries out all physical brutality for Sue's illegal crimes and deals.

Stone: Ann's father, a stupid old fool in his mid- fifties. He is addicted to gambling. For his debts he sold his own daughter. He is always in need of money and does not care about his own family and children.

Pete: An evil thug, around fifty years old. He is one of the members of an organized crime ring. He is Sue's buddy in all illegal dealings, specializing in smuggling, drug trafficking, gambling and prostitution.

Flor: A woman around fifty. A long term pimp. She is the most vile,cruel devil that any one can imagine. She also runs a small, illegal house of prostitution.

DAISY: A young woman around twenty. She is a stowaway, illegally brought into the country by Pete and his company. She is illiterate, simple minded and very vain.

Kit: A cute girl of eighteen, she is a friend of May's; they come from the same hometown. Both were smuggled into the country for prostitution. She is also uneducated and illiterate, but retains a sense of self respect and a touch of innocence.

Coral: A police officer of the district, she is honest and dedicated but there is little she can do by the book.

Young: Jade's former school teacher. Came from the same island off the coast. She has known Jade and her mother for a long time. Jade asked for her help after being abducted but it was too late by the time she got there.

4

Act 1

Time: A hot summer afternoon in June.

Scenery: The living room, bedroom, and back room.

Characters: Ann, Jade, Rose, Sue, Clint, Stone, Flor, Pete, Officer
Coral

When the curtains go up, there is a bright red sunset outside. Sue sits
in the living room, waving a fan and using a handkerchief to
wipe her face; she looks angry. Ann is in the bedroom, sitting
in the corner, looking scared. In the back room, the audience
can hear the sound of whip, followed by a young woman's
scream.

Jade: (In the back,crying and yelling) No, I won't do it. You can go
ahead and kill me, I just won't do it.

Sue: (Gets angry, rises and waves her fan) O.K. ! Clint, give her some
more, I want to see who is tougher. (Lights a cigarette)

Clint: Yes, ma'am. (more whip sounds and crying)

Sue: You are in my hands now. If you don't obey, you are going to
learn the hard way what it means to defy me. I'll whip the skin
right off your back if I have to.

Jade: No, I will never do it . I would rather die than sell my body. Go
right ahead, kill me, I don't care.

Sue: Oh, I can't let you die, not after what I had to pay for you. I just
want you to know who is in control here. Clint, stop the whip,
use the cigarette, burn the middle of her palm.

Clint: Yes, Ma'am. (screaming from the back room)

(Ann hides in the corner of her room, scared, holding her head,
shaking and crying)

5

(The screams suddenly stop)

Sue: What happened, Clint?

Clint: She passed out...............

   Sue: Spray her with some cold water; wake her up and bring her back to her room. Starve her for three days, then we'll see.

(Audience hears the sound of water being spat from Clint's mouth, then Jade's painful moaning. The door opens, Clint drags Jade out, Jade looks horrible, bloodstains on her torn clothing. Clint throws her onto the bed, turns around and grabs Ann from the corner)

Clint: Now it's your turn; let's go. (grabs Ann and pulls her out of the room. Locks the door from the outside, then takes Ann into the other room where Jade took the beating. Jade, seeing him leave, sits up slowly and checking her wounds, starts to weep. The lights dim to dark)

Sue: (Yelling toward the back room) Just give her a good beating; I can't believe that they won't obey me. (Screaming and whipping noises from the back room)

Ann: Stop, please stop, I can't take it any more............I'll do whatever you say, no more, no more...........

Sue: O.K. Clint, stop. As long as she's willing to obey. Untie her and lock her in a different room.

   Clint: Yes, Ma'am.

(Sue sits down and pours herself a cup of tea to drink. Rose comes in from the outside)

Rose: Ma'am, I'm back.

Sue: You're back? So soon? What happened? You just left a little while ago.

Rose: That old man didn't take long at all, what can I do?

Sue: Useless old fools. Where's the money?

Rose: (Takes money out of her pocket) It's all here.

Sue: (Counts the money and gets angry) The clerk at the hotel said it would be a thousand, how come It's only eight hundred ?

Rose: The clerk took two hundred for a service charge. It's routine; I couldn't do a thing about it.

Sue: I see. (Gives a fifty dollar bill to Rose) This is for you.

Rose: Thank you Ma'am. I'm going in to clean up.

Sue: Wait a minute. You come here. (Rose walks toward Sue) Let me check, take off your shoes. (Sue checks her shoes, hair bow, body and can't find anything. Finally, she finds a hundred dollar bill folded tightly in her bra) You thought I couldn't find it if you hid it in your bra? (Slaps Rose across her face) What do you think I am? If I ever catch you keeping money from me again, I'll throw you out on the street, naked.

Rose: (Crying) I didn't keep it from you. It's mine! The customer gave it to me as a tip.

Sue: Tip? I told you, you give me every nickel and dime that you make. You hear? I paid money to own you; every piece of your hair and skin is owned by me. If it wasn't because I'm so kind and sweet, you wouldn't get fifty dollars spending money. Do you understand ?

Rose: Yes, Ma'am.

Sue: Oh, by the way, while you were gone, your boyfriend, Ted, stopped by. He was looking for you, mumbling something about wanting to buy you out from me and marry you. God knows what he's thinking about.

Rose: He's a nice guy. He truly loves me. He told me that as soon as he finishes his service, he'll tell his parents and get me out of here. He wants me to wait for him.

Sue: Is his family rich?

7

Rose: His family's from the south, not too rich but they own a lot of land. Recently they sold some for development and made a lot of money. I don't think he would lie to me about that.

Sue: Dear Rose, open your eyes, don't ever believe any man's words. When they want to please you, they will say anything; nowadays nothing is dependable except your own money.

Rose: Don't worry; if Ted doesn't have money, I won't go with him. One way or another you'll get your money back.

Sue: Well, I'm glad that you feel that way. You must be smart, don't do anything stupid you hear? I have been sweet to you, haven't I?

Rose: Yes Ma'am. I'd better go now. (Rose goes into one of the rooms)

(Clint brings Ann out from another room)

Clint: Ma'am, she's thirsty. She wants some water; what should I do?

Sue: (Says to Ann) You're not tied up, are you? If you want water, get it yourself!

Ann: Thank you Ma'am. (She looks weak, walking slowly toward the table for water. Her torn clothing is splotched with blood stains.)

Sue: (Looking at Ann) Clint, she's O. K., I'll watch her. I don't think she has the nerve to get away now. You'd better go and guard the front gate.

Clint: Yes, Ma'am. (Exits off stage through the main entrance)

Sue: Ann, you come here......... Sit down..........You listen to me, you are smarter than that idiot Jade. She is stubborn and asking for punishment. I'll lock her in the dark room for three days without anything, We'll see who's the boss around here, won't we?

Ann: Ma'am, let me be your maid to serve you. (on her knees) I'll do anything for you, I'll cook, I'll wash, and clean the house, bathroom........ anything, but please don't make me sell my body........

8

Sue: What? Complaining again? Aren't you afraid that I'll burn you with a cigarette?

Ann: Oh, no, I'm not complaining. I just don't want to be a prostitute. It is the most degrading thing, I cannot bring myself to stoop so low......

Sue: Degrading, huh? Having no money at all is the real degrading thing. Ann, if it was not for your father owing a lot of money, and selling you to me, I could never force you to stoop this low, right? What do you want to be, a princess?

Ann: I am still young, I am useless for your customers now. Why don't you wait until I get older, then use me.

Sue: Nonsense, your father told me that you were raped once before, and you've already started your period. I know that you're fully developed. What are you afraid of?

Ann: (thinking about it for a while) How long must I do this for you Ma'am?

Sue: It was clearly stated in the contract with your father; didn't he tell you?

Ann: No, my father didn't say anything. He just told me to behave myself and listen to you and that you would give me room and board.

Sue: I paid your father three hundred and fifty thousand in cash. In return, you will work for me for five years to pay off the loan and the interest.

Ann: Five years? That is a long time, by then I should be in college.

Sue: No, it's not that long. Some of my girls have stayed here for most of their lives. Now you are fifteen, in five years, you will only be twenty, still very young. If you so wish, you may continue to work for me then, we split 60/40. I guarantee that you will make a fortune. After that you can still marry and live happily ever after.

Ann: I can't think that far ahead. How many men do I have to take a day?

Sue: It is hard to say; if you are sweet to your customers, twenty clients a day is very common. If the business isn't good, not many customers, then I won't even be able to feed you.

Ann: Do I give you all the money I make ?

Sue: Of course, otherwise how would you be able to pay me back? Why should I feed you for nothing?

(Suddenly, the alarm system goes off)

Sue: Clint! Clint!

Clint: (Rushes in from main entrance) Yes, Ma'am, you called?

Sue: The alarm system just went off, go to the back and see if there's someone trying to escape.

Clint: Yes, Ma'am, right away. (Exits stage from one of the rooms on the left side of the stage)

Sue: Ann, let me tell you, I have alarm systems here, with guards stationed at all doors that lead to the outside. Don't even bother trying to escape. I have your I. D. card, without it you can't get a job and no one would dare to keep you. I also have people working for me on the streets as well. When I catch those who try to escape from me, the punishment is so severe that they wish they were dead before it even starts.

Ann: Yes, I know. Ma'am, I am very hungry, may I have something to eat?

Sue: Of course, you may. As I told you, as long as you listen, I'll treat you well.

Clint: (Coming out from one of the left rooms) Ma'am, I checked, no one is missing. Probably the cat touched one of the sensors. Don't worry, every thing is intact.

Sue: All right, you go and get Rose for me now.

Clint: (walking towards the left of the stage and yelling) Rose, Madam is calling you, please come out now. (After Rose answers, Clint exits the stage through the main entrance)

Rose: (Comes in through one of the doors from the left) Yes, ma'am, you called? You have a customer for me?

Sue: No, not guests. It is Ann; she's hungry. Will you take her to the kitchen, get her something to eat? Then clean her up and put some makeup on her.

Rose: Yes, ma'am.

Sue: Also, lend her one of your pretty dresses. She is willing to receive guests now. She ought to look half decent. You are older and have more experience, look after her and teach her a few tricks. By the way, take care of the bruises on her face, we don't want to spoil our guests' appetite, do we?

Rose: Yes, Ma'am. I know; I'll take care of it. Come with me, Ann; call me Rose.

Ann: Thank you, Rose.

Rose: Don't mention it, it's my pleasure.

(Ann and Rose exit on the left, Clint comes in from right side main entrance)

Clint: Ma'am, Ms. Flor is here to see you.

Sue: Great, show her in.

Clint: (Yells, walking toward the door) Ms. Flor, Madam asks that you come in, please.

Flor: (Enters, all dressed up) Sue, how are you? How is the business?

Sue: I am fine, thank you, Flor, everything is just fine. Clint, pour tea for Ms. Flor. Look at you, all dressed up. You look prettier every day.

Flor: (laughs) Oh, you...... Speak for yourself. (Clint brings the tea over for Flor, then exits through the main entrance) I just stopped by to say hello, and to check and see how Rose is doing?

Sue: She is doing fine; not too bad. Do you have any new ones for me?

Flor: Maybe. I have some relatives. The husband was a sailor and is in jail for smuggling. The wife is paralyzed in bed. Two daughters, one is thirteen, and the other one is eleven. Both are good looking and developed quite well. I'd be doing a good deed to help them out. Would you be interested?

Sue: (Looking doubtful) Don't you think they might be a bit too young? I would have to feed them at least a couple of years before they are useful; I don't know.............

Flor: The price is good and negotiable. They can help out around here first. In a couple of years, they'll be just at the right age to start. Anyway, I heard that the current trend is with the "milk teeth" ones. Can you imagine how much money they would bring in for you? They would truly be your money tree.

Sue: For goodness' sake, you couldn't be more right. You know everything.

Flor: Their mother said that if you're not interested, she will send them to a bar for the porno "Body Show".

Sue: Oh, no, not those, they wouldn't make much money at all. They're better off with me. All right, because of you, I'll take a look at them, and we'll see how it goes from there.

Flor: I know you are a smart business woman. You would never miss a good deal. I'll show them to you first, before we discuss the price.

Sue: Are they outside now? Hurry up and bring them in.

Flor: No.......... I didn't bring them with me. I know the newspaper has recently run some articles on minors in illegal prostitution. The police are under a lot of pressure to clean up your district. I

12

kept them in a coffee shop on the corner to wait for me. If you have time, I'll personally take you there.

Sue: You are perfect, very professional. Let's go . (Yells for Clint, he comes right in) Clint, I am going out with Ms. Flor for a few minutes. You stay here and watch things for me.

Clint: Yes, ma'am. Don't you worry, I'll take care of things here.

Sue: You better; if I lose any of them, I'll have your hide.

Clint: Yes, I know, don't worry.

(Sue and Flor exit the stage through the main entrance. Clint goes into the closet, getting out a bottle of wine. He turns on the radio, and, finding himself a chair, he drinks and listens to the radio. The lights gradually dim. The clock on the wall chimes. A while later, Rose, with a cosmetics case in one hand and holding Ann's hand with the other, brings her to the center of the living room. They both sit down. Ann has cleaned up, put on some makeup and a pretty dress. She looks different and quite attractive)

Rose: (looks at Ann) Ann, how did your father come to owe so much money?

Ann: It's all because of his gambling. He used to be a good mason and made a nice living. A year ago, his friends started him gambling. In the beginning, they let him win a couple of times. He got hooked on the excitement, and now he's addicted to it.

Rose: Yes, I have heard that the organized crime rings operate those Lotto games and underground casinos. They get you hooked and control your life from then on.

Ann: You can say that again! All my dad wants to do everyday now is to win his lost money back. They designed it in a way, however, that he just keeps at it and loses more and more. Finally, I became the sacrificial lamb.

Rose: Where is your mother? Doesn't she say anything?

13

Ann: My mother couldn't stop my father from gambling. She divorced
     him and left us. I guess she figured that she couldn't support
     us kids if she took us with her.

Rose: Have you ever tried to locate her? To let her know what's
      happened to you?

Ann: No, the last I heard, she was working at a piano bar. There are so
     many of them in the city, how would I know where to start?

Rose: Don't feel bad; compared to mine, your life is ten times
      better........... I was an orphan, raised by my grandmother. We
      were hungry most of the time. At times, when I couldn't stand it
      any more, I had to steal the food from the altars in the temples.
      When my grandmother died, I was sold by one of my distant
      relatives to pay for her funeral.

Ann: Oh, dear, how sad. We are all unfortunate people.

(The light over Clint gradually turns bright. Clint rises from his seat,
     rather drunk, discovers them, walks towards Ann. Surprised by
     her looks, he stares at her)

Clint: Hey...... now that you've gotten cleaned up, I almost didn't
       recognize you. Come on, come and keep me company.
       (grabs Ann's hand)

Ann: No, leave me alone.

Rose: Where is Madam.

Clint: She is out, I'm in charge for the moment. You all have to obey
       me now. Come on Rose, give me a kiss and call me something
       sweet. (Clint approaches them as they back away. He grabs
       Rose, kissing her while she resists) Come on! Whisper some
       sweet nothings in my ear!

Rose: (reluctantly) Dear Clint, sweet heart.

Clint: That's right, this is more like it. Come, have a drink with me (Gets
       a glass and pours some wine for Rose)

Rose: Fine, I'll have a drink. (She drinks it up)

Clint: Bottoms up, wonderful! (Clint drinks up and pours another glass, handing it to Ann) Come on, Ann, your turn now, have a drink, go ahead, take it.

Ann: No, I don't drink.

Rose: Ann, take it. If you don't, he won't leave you alone.

Clint: That's right, take it.

Ann: No, I don't know how to drink. I don't want it.

Clint: Damn you, you never learn. (Throws the whole glass of wine in Ann's face) You stupid bitch! I'm nice to you, and I get nowhere. Fine, you won't drink with me, I'll make you sleep with me now. I'll show you who's Boss. (Proceeds to grab at her, as Ann runs away from him)

Ann: No, I don't want to........no.........no!

Clint: You don't want to? But I want to. (Rushes up, grabs her, kisses her and touches her all over. Ann fights against him, screaming and pleading, while Rose tries to separate them)

Rose: Come on, Clint, don't be like this. Ann is still too young to understand. Please leave her alone. (approaches and tries to stop him)

Clint: Don't try to stop me. (pushes Rose away) I know what I am doing.......... I must teach this idiot a lesson; to show her how I really can be................

(Clint picks Ann up and walks towards the back. As she is kicking and screaming, Ann's father, Stone, enters. He looks dishevelled, holding a paper bag in his hand)

Stone: Ann!

(Clint, surprised by another person in the room, drops Ann on the floor. Ann quickly gets up and runs to her father holding on to him and crying)

Ann: Dad..........(crying)

Clint: (Realizing it is only Stone, his face twists angrily again) Oh, it's
      you. You already sold her to us, what the hell are you doing
      here?

Stone: I just wanted to visit her a bit. Ann, how are you doing?

Ann: Oh, Dad, please take me home.

Stone: (Helplessly look away, then changes the subject) Ann, are you
      hungry? I brought you something to eat. Try some, will you?

Ann: No, I just had some food, I'm not hungry.

Clint: Your daughter has a mind of her own; she's been here almost a
      week and refuses to go to work. You better tell her to wise up
      for her own good, she should be more cooperative.

Stone: Please, Clint, I would be most grateful if you'd kindly smooth
      things over.

Clint: Rose, take them to the bedroom to talk, I'm busy here.

(All three of them go into the room at the left front of the stage, they
      turn on the light and the main stage lights dim.

Rose: (After Ann and Stone sit down) You two have a nice chat. I've
      got a few things to do, myself. I'll see you later. (Rose leaves
      the room and exits the stage)

Stone: You keep this.......... (gives her the paper bag) Ann........ I'm
      sorry that you are here.

Ann: Dad, I don't like it here. I don't want to sell my body. I am so afraid
      of the madam and that thug. They are evil; they are worse
      than animals. They are not treating us like human beings.

Stone: Ann, I'm sorry, I............

Ann: (shows Stone her wounds from the beating, Stone looks, eyes
      expressive of his pain) Dad, look at what they did to me. If it
      wasn't for my giving in today, they were going to use a cigarette
      to burn me.

Stone: (Painfully) Ann, please listen to me; try to go along with them
    so you avoid the physical pain. I sold you because I had to.
    You know I needed the money.

Ann: That's always your problem, you always need the money, to do
    what? More bets!

Stone: You know that I had no choice. If I didn't pay them back the
    money that I owed, they were going to waste me. If that
    happened, who would feed your brother and sisters?

Ann: You brought the whole thing upon yourself by joining those
    hoodlums. Why aren't you stopping it now?

Stone: Now I'm just gambling to win my lost money back. Don't you
    think that I want our family to have a better life?

Ann: No, I don't believe you. You only think of yourself; you never
    gave a damn about the family. How could you have sold me to
    this place? How am I going to survive here? I hate you! (Starts
    to cry)

Stone: You're right; I am a selfish old fool. I'm so sorry to put you
    through this.

Ann: Dad, if you give me some money, I'll try to run away. If I found my
    mother, she might help me.

Stone: Don't even bother; I heard that your mother remarried and
    moved abroad.

Ann: Are you sure? I can't believe it.

Stone: It's true, why would I lie to you? Besides, I have no money on
    hand any way. The truth is that I'm here to see whether Madam
    will lend me more.

Ann: (Disappointed) Then you didn't really come to see me, did you?
    You're just trying to get more money so that you can continue
    your betting! You don't give a damn about me!.........(Starts to
    cry)

Stone: Ann, stop this. You're going to make me cry, too. (Both are
    crying and the lights start to dim)

(The living room lights turns bright. Sue comes in from the main
        entrance, Clint was sitting there smoking, but as soon as he
        sees her, he hurries to hide the wine bottle)

Clint: Oh, you're back, how was the business deal?

Sue: We couldn't agree upon the price. I deliberately put it off for a few
        days to see how it goes.

Clint: You're very smart in business, you are, Ma'am. By the way, Ann's
        father is here.

Sue: I see. Oh, on my way home, my informer told me that the police
        are coming for a special inspection. Make sure that the girls
        who have no license are out of sight. And tell Ann's father to
        get the hell out of here; I don't want to be bothered.

Clint: Yes ma'am, right away. (Exits stage through the left door)

Sue: (gets a cigarette out, lights it, calculating out loud) Only thirteen,
        and they ask for two hundred thousand.......No, no way, who
        do they think they are?

Stone: (Comes out of the left bed room) How are you today, Ma'am? I
        stopped by to discuss............I want.....I want to.........

Sue: What do you want, come on, say it.

Stone: I want to borrow some money. I have some inside tips on
        today's bets, I know that I have a good chance of winning.

Sue: No way. You'd better leave, the police will be here any minute.
        You better get out of the way. (Starts to push Stone out)

Stone: All right, I'm going, maybe some other day, O. K.? I'll be back.
        (Off stage)

(Phone rings, Sue picks it up)

Sue: Yes, what? .... Oh, a Japanese tourist!.....young?
        ....how young? don't worry, I guarantee they'll be under
        sixteen and able to speak Japanese. Fine, no problem, it's
        eight thousand per girl, they will be there after midnight............

What? Now? If I send them now, I'll have to charge double.......... Yes.......... O.K. What hotel?........ Dianna, and the room number is?......... 520. All right, I got it, they are on their way. (hangs up the phone)

Sue: Clint, come here.

Clint: (Shows up from left) Yes, ma'am. The girls are well hidden.

Sue: Good, I just got a phone call . We have some customers at the Dianna Hotel, room 520. Take Mimi and Jasmine there right now; use the back door.

Clint: Yes, ma'am, I'll leave with them right now. (Exits stage from the left door)

(Police officer, Coral, enters through main entrance)

Coral: Anyone here?

Sue: Oh, hello, Officer Coral, how are you today? To what do we owe this honor? Inspection again? Sit, please......cigarette?

Coral: No, thank you, I don't smoke.

Sue: In that case, have some tea. (Pours tea, putting it next to Coral)

Coral: Ms. Sue, this morning, in the Daily News, there was a letter written from a girl, asking for help. She claims that she's been held against her will at your place for a week now, her name is Jade, and she's from out of town. What do you have to say about this?

Sue: My dear Officer, the accusation is ridiculous. All my girls here are licensed. They are all registered with permission to work. If you don't believe me, you may go ahead and check for yourself.

Coral: Come on, let's not kid ourselves, do you have Jade here or not?

Sue: If you don't want to take my word for it, you may search the premises.

Coral: Let me warn you now; forcing anybody into prostitution is inhumane and illegal. If I catch you, I'll see to it personally that you lose your license and wind up in jail.

Sue: I know; don't you worry, I'm not that stupid. (Changes her tone of voice) You and I have known each other for a long time and I've always been very fond of you. In fact, I have something here for you. (As she talks, she takes some money, places it in an envelope and hands it over to Coral) It merely expresses my gratitude for your hard work in our district.

Coral: No, thank you. I'm here for official business only. I'll will not have any thing to do with your sinful money. (Coral proceeds to search the backroom)

Sue: Hey, if you don't want it, it's your loss. Trying to make me feel ashamed? Don't even bother.

(Pete comes in from outside dressed in a flashy style. He moves intimately towards Sue)

Pete: Hello, my dear sweet Boss, do you still remember me? I haven't seen you for two months! You're looking better than ever.

Sue: (Returning as warmly) For heaven's sake, it's you. I hadn't heard from you in so long, I thought you were dead and rotting in some God forsaken place.

Pete: Oh, come on, don't say such horrible things, you'll give me bad luck. If I had been dead, whatever would you have done without me? Let me explain, what happened was that I took a business trip with my Boss. But you were always on my mind (Gives her a present and proceeds to fondle her as she opens it) Do you like it? Try it on.

Sue: (Puts the bracelet on her wrist, raises her arm examining it) Mmm...... This is more like it. It's beautiful; is it real, or just a fake?

Pete: My dear! Me? Pete? I'd never even touch the fake stuff! Especially for you!

Sue: All right, all right, thank you for not forgetting about me. I have a police officer doing a random inspection. As soon as she leaves, we'll go out to eat; my treat to welcome you home.

Pete: Great, let's do that. I haven't been here in so long, do you mind if I stay the night? (Starts to fondle her again)

Sue: Stop, stop. Can't you wait? I know you must be as horny as hell, but get a hold of yourself, we have all night.

Pete: All right, I'll listen to you now, but later you'll be listening to me...........

Sue: Come on, be serious now, where did you go? Tell me about it.

Pete: We went to Mainland China, traveled through many cities. The standard of living is still so low there, with our money we were treated like kings. We definitely got our money's worth. I must say, nowadays, it doesn't matter who you are, if you have money, no matter where you go, you're the Boss.

Sue: I bet! No wonder you didn't want to come back. Tell me the truth, how many women did you have over there?

Pete: Don't be jealous, I am here for you now, what more do you want?

(Officer Coral enters on stage from left)

Sue: Officer Coral, how does everything look to you? As I told you before, I follow the rules and regulations by the book. There is nothing illegal to be found here.

Coral: Yes, so far so good. I'd better get going. (She exits through the main entrance)

Sue: (Yells to the departing officer) It is always good to see you! Come any time!

Pete: (Grabs Sue) Hey! Boy, have I got a good business deal for you. I guarantee you'll make a bundle of money over this.

Sue: What's that? Tell me about it.

Pete: On our trip we discovered some promising new business potential.

Sue: Yes...... what?

Pete: We established some connections. They'll use fishing boats to smuggle young girls to us. The price is good, the girls are young and pretty. Most of them are illiterate, and will have nobody to complain to or run to. You really can handle them any way you want.

Sue: That sounds great, but are you sure you can get them?

Pete: Yes, positive. This way, you'll never have to worry about your supply of girls. Your business will boom.

Sue: I'll rely on you to arrange this whole deal, O. K?

Pete: Of course, I'll take care of it. Just don't forget my commission.

Sue: For heaven's sake, don't I always pay you well and take good care of you?

Pete: I know, that's why I'm giving this deal to you, exclusively. At the rate you're going, pretty soon you'll be a millionaire. You'd better not forget about me! (They are necking when Rose rushes in)

Rose: Madam, something terrible has happened!

Sue: What's wrong?!

Rose: Jade, she jumped from her window and ran away.

Sue: What? Ran away from me? That damn fool! Clint! You stupid idiot, how did you let her get away?

Pete: Don't worry, we'll get her back. With the number of snitches we have on the streets, we'll get her back in no time at all.

Sue: Damn it, go and catch her; then, bring her back to me! I'll fix her.

END OF ACT ONE

ACT TWO

Time: A month later.

Scene: Same as before.

Characters: Sue, Pete, Daisy, Kit, Clint, Rose, Ann, Stone, Young, Flor, Jade, Coral.

When curtains rise,Sue and Pete are drinking and eating, enjoying themselves.

Pete: Come on, darling, have another one, let's toast to our success. (Pours wine for both)

Sue: Yes, I'll drink to that. Bottoms up.

Pete: Dear, didn't I tell you? I wasn't kidding when I said that I could find a good supply for you. You see, less than a month, I got what you wanted. You'll make a bundle over these two.

Sue: Yes, I thank you for that. But I'm a little bit worried, if we get caught, I wonder what kind of mess we'd be in?

Pete: Don't worry, if by some chance we do get caught, I'll take care of it. It only takes a little money to make these troubles go away, no big deal. Come on, drink some more, here's to you.......... Let me tell you, as long as you have me on your side, no matter what happens, I'll handle it, you won't ever have to worry about anything.

Sue: Thank you! By the way, when you brought them here, I heard you telling them that they were here for manual labor. If they find out what they really have to do, do you think they'll resist and give me any trouble?

23

Pete: Don't worry, I have it all figured out. The first few days, take them out shopping, sight seeing, let them have some fun. After you've got them adapted to a finer manner of living, they'll love their new life style so much and be so in debt to you, they'll do anything you want them to.

Sue: Of course, I had all that in mind already.

Pete: Besides, they lived in such poverty before. When they find out how much money they can make by going along with you, I bet they won't give you any problems at all.

Sue: Marvellous, I raise a toast to you! (Phone rings, Sue answers it) Yes, who is this?........Hold on, let me get him for you............ (lowers her voice to Pete) It's for you, I think it's your Boss.

Pete: (Takes the phone, seriously) Yes, sir, this is Pete. Tomorrow.............. I'll take care of the shipment............No, no problem.......... I know, I'm going right now. (hangs up the phone)   Darling, I have to take care of some business, I've got to run.

Sue: Fine, will you be back tonight?

Pete: I don't know for sure. I'll give you a call later.

Sue: You have more "people" coming? If you do, I could always use more pretty ones.

Pete: No, it's not "people", it's these... (drawing a gun from his jacket)

Sue: Illegal firearms?

Pete: That's right. It's a very profitable business. Don't mention it to anyone. I don't need any trouble.

Sue: Of course not; I'm with you.

Pete: Come, let's drink this, then, I've got to go. (they finish up their drinks, Pete rushes out through the main entrance)

(Sue turns on the radio, tuning in to some pop songs, and continues drinking, eating by herself)

(After a while, Daisy and Kit enter through the left room. They're
         dressed in new but flashy clothing, hairdos,and make up. They
         appear to be very satisfied with their looks.)

Sue: (Seeing these two, stops eating) Have you both eaten?

Daisy: Yes, ma'am, we just ate. (Kit nods her head, too)

Sue: You both look beautiful. Do your clothes fit well? Do you like
        them?

Daisy: Yes, I love them. (Kit nods her head again)

Sue: Who put the makeup on you? She did a good job.

Kit: LuLu did it, I've never put anything on my face before.

Sue: After all, it took some effort to get you here, I certainly wouldn't
        mistreat you. How do you like it so far?

Kit: I love it here.

Sue: Are you happy here, Daisy?

Daisy: Yes, I am. I've been so excited, I have trouble going to sleep at
        night.

Sue: As I understand it, neither of you can read. Is this true?

Kit: Yes, it's true. I only know how to write my name, but Daisy can't
        even do that. Is that alright?

Sue: Oh, of course, it's no problem at all. Do you have any relatives
        here? Let me know, I'll locate them for you.

Daisy: No, we don't have any.

Sue: Are you sure? It's no trouble at all, really you can tell me.

Daisy: Yes, we know, but we really don't know anybody here.

Kit: I swear, we don't have any relatives around here. Ma'am, when do
        we start working? How much do we get a month?

Sue: Oh, there's no rush, take it easy, get some rest, first. I'll have someone show you the town, let you two have some fun first. As far as the pay, I guarantee you at least ten times as much as you made before.

Daisy: Really? Oh my goodness, are you sure this is true?

Sue: Of course, it's true. That's why people always want to come here to work, for the high pay.

Kit: I've heard about it, but I didn't know it would be this good!

Daisy: This is wonderful, Kit! We're going to have a good life from now on.

(Sue rings the bell on the table, Clint comes in through the main entrance)

Clint: Yes, ma'am, you rang for me?

Sue: Clint, are you busy now?

Clint: No, Ma'am.

Sue: Good. (Opens her handbag, gets out some money, and hands it to Clint) Here, take some money with you and show them the town. Buy them some jewelry or anything they want that'll make them look good. Keep them happy, you hear?

Clint: Yes, I'll do my best...............I think I need more........

Sue: O.K. Here's some more. (Turning to Daisy and Kit) I am lending this to you. (Waving her money) When you two start working, don't forget to pay me back.

Daisy: Yes, ma'am.

Kit: Thank you.

Sue: Clint, they are strangers in town, make sure that they don't get lost.

Clint: Don't you worry, ma'am; don't I have the reputation of finding our lost girls? Huh..........?

Sue: Fine, keep up your good work.

(All three say good by and leave from main entrance)

(After a while, Ann and Rose enter from the main entrance. Both look
       like wounded soldiers. Blood stains are visible on their torn
       clothing, and they looked pained and tired)

Rose: Ma'am, we're back.

Sue: Oh, my goodness, what happened to you two? Why are you so
       late? Look at you, did you get into a fight with someone ? Both
       of you? What a mess.

Rose: In the hotel room, we ran into a few thugs. They were drunk,
       they beat us up, nearly killed us.   Look at here..... and
       here.......look at Ann's face.......

Sue: (Checks them out) I don't believe this, how could this happen?
       Where is the money?

Ann: Why can't you believe us? There were seven of them.   They
       were nasty and brutal. One of them showed me a gun and said
       that we were lucky that they didn't kill us, and we'd better forget
       about the money.

Sue: Damn, how dare they. Did you ask them what gang they
       belonged to? Perhaps I'll have to deal with their boss.

Rose: I was scared to death, I figured we'd better just forget about the
       whole thing. One of them said that they weren't afraid of
       anything, and that they had just killed a policeman last week.
       The one with the gun pointed at me said that if we go to the
       police, they'll get us all.

Sue: They really said so? Don't lie to me.

Ann: I swear, I'm not lying.

Sue: Rose, what do you have to say?

Rose: You can't lie about this kind of thing. I was being held at gun point, for God's sake. If you don't believe me, search me; go ahead.

Sue: All right, I'll take your word for it. Next time you'd better use your head and be more alert.

Rose: There is no more next time, I don't want to make calls on strangers anymore.

Sue: Don't be afraid; from now on, I'll have Clint take you girls and act as a bodyguard. Now, go get some rest.

Rose: Yes, thank you. (as both exit left off the stage, they are halted by Sue)

Sue: Just a minute, I almost forgot. Since we caught Jade, I've had her locked in that dark room for three days now. I've probably starved her into being a little more cooperative. Go get some food for her. She is more useful to me alive than dead. While you are at it, tell her there is no way to get out of my hands. She is better off cooperating with me, if she wants to live.

Rose: Ma'am, you better not push her too hard, otherwise, she might kill herself.

Sue: I can't believe she really wants to die. Ann, you tell her, I have not used my worst tactics yet. Even if she is made of steel, I have ways handling her. I would skin her alive, if I had too.

(Ann looks shocked, her mouth hangs open as she stares at Sue)

Rose: Ann, don't just stand there, let's go.

(As they are leaving, Stone walks in from the main entrance, Ann sees him, turns around and rushes towards him)

Ann: Dad, it's so good to see you here. Are you taking me home with you? Please get me out of here, I can't take it any more.

Stone: Ann, what's happened to you? Who did this to you? (Stone touches her face and looks sorry)

Sue: I didn't do it. It was her own bad luck, she ran into some thugs and got beaten.

Stone: Oh........You have to be more careful.

Sue: Rose, you go and take care of things for me.

Rose: Yes, ma'am. (Exits stage from left door)

Sue: Stone, you may go to Ann's room to have a chat with her. I have to run my business here.

Stone: Thank you.... actually, I'm here to see you.

Sue: See me? What can I do for you?

Stone: Ann, you go and clean up first, I'll talk to Madam for few minutes.

Ann: Dad, are you going to take me home?

Stone: Don't interrupt now, I'll talk to you later.

Ann: Yes, Dad. (Ann exits from left door)

Stone: Ma'am........(Scratches his head and neck, looking for words) I wonder...........Is it possible for you to lend me two hundred thousand? I have a good chance to triple my money this time.

Sue: Are you still gambling?

Stone: I just can't believe that I can't win my lost money back. I've won it before. Last night, I had a dream; my luck is changing and I'm going to be on a winning streak.

Sue: Stone, what if you lose again? How am I going to get my money back?

Stone: Well, so far, I'm leasing Ann to you for five years. If I can't pay you back, I'll add another three years onto the lease.

Sue: That sounds reasonable. It doesn't bother you? How about Ann? Will she go along with it?

Stone: I think so, she is a good girl. She has always listened to me. I don't see any problem.

Sue: Stone, I think you should clear your head, and think it over again.

Stone: I've thought about it many times. Please, help me out this time, I beg you to give me another chance. I just want to get my money back....... I guarantee you, I'll pay you back with high interest........ Ann is in your possession, what do you have to lose?

Sue: I am not a bank. It would be better if you went to someone else.

Stone: I have no one else to go to, you are my only hope to get my money back.

Sue: Other than Ann, don't you have some other children? If so, how old are they?

Stone: My second daughter is fourteen, third daughter is ten and my son is only seven.

Sue: In that case, I'll take your second daughter as collateral for two hundred thousand.

Stone: My second daughter? She's too young; she's not even developed yet.

Sue: Fourteen is good enough, you let me be the judge. Some of my best customers love the young ones. A few hormone shots will take care of it. How about it? Do we have a deal?

Stone: I.......I.........I'm afraid people will think that I am too cruel.

Sue: You're afraid of criticism? Come on, you've got to be kidding.

Stone: (Scratches his head, thinking, unable to make up his mind)

Sue: You don't want to? That's O.K. I won't force you. You better go, I have to get back to my business.

Stone: (Thinks about it for a while, and makes up his mind) All right, give me the money, and I'll sign your contract.

Sue: I can write you a check, but I don't want you to regret it later.

Stone: Regret?........ (showing his inner conflict, then decidedly) No, I won't regret it.......... I know this time I'll win and I will pay you back; I won't lose her.

(Ann rushes out from inside room, grabs her father)

Ann: No, Dad, you can't gamble any more. You sold me and ruined me, isn't that enough? Lily is still too young, to even understand it.......... You can't bring her here to torture her and make her suffer like me! (Starts to cry and beg) Dad, I beg you, please spare her, please.......Oh, dear God help us..........

Stone: (Embarassed) Ann, you overheard everything?

Ann: Dad, say no more, please go....... If you do it, you will no longer be my father, and May will hate you forever too.

Stone: (appears to come to his senses) Ann, I'm sorry, I must have been possessed by the devil. I almost made another sinful mistake, please forgive me.

Ann: Dad, one wrong thing is bad enough, please don't do it again. The little ones are waiting for you to take care of them, please go home. (pushes Stone toward the door)

(Sue clears off the table. Ann goes back to her room. Ms. Young enters through the front entrance)

Young: Excuse me, is this number 44?

Sue: (Stares at her suspiciously) What are you doing here?

Young: Are you.....?

Sue: I am the owner of this establishment. What can I do for you?

Young: I am looking for a girl named Jade, by any chance, is she here?

Sue: Jade? We don't have anyone named Jade here, you must have the wrong address.

Young: Ma'am, let me introduce myself. I am a school teacher, Jade was my student. To make a long story short, we both came from a small island off the coast. She had been an exceptional student, so her mother let her come to the city, for advanced studies. It so happened that I was in the same town so her mother asked me to look after her. I got her a job during the day, and she was going to school at night. Everything seemed to be working out fine. Last month, she suddenly disappeared. After searching for her for a while, I was told that a young hoodlum not only cheated her but also abducted her to this address............

Sue: Nonsense, what proof do you have?

Young: Two weeks ago, I got a letter from her, asking me to come and save her. Here is the letter, with your address on it, is this good enough proof?

Sue: (Taking a look at the letter head) This happened a long time ago. Why didn't you come right away?

Young: I was in charge of the entrance examinations at the school; I could not get away immediately.

Sue: You're too late, she ran away shortly after she got here. I'm looking for her myself.

Young: What? She really got away from here?!

Sue: Yes, I bet she's at one of those shelters. The homes for runaway teenagers, you must know about those.

Young: Are you sure that she's not here?

Sue: Ms. Young, I paid four hundred thousand for her. If you find her, tell her that I'll need compensation for my losses. Otherwise, I won't let her get off the hook so easily.

Young: (surprised and convinced) All right, I'll try some other places. (Exits through main entrance)

(After a while Flor comes in through the main entrance, all dressed up)

Sue: Oh, my goodness, Flor, you are getting younger every day. To what do I owe the honor?

Flor: I heard that you got two gorgeous new girls. I came especially to meet them. I heard that they're your money trees now.

Sue: What money tree? I've run into such bad luck, lately. I've got a stubborn tree stump on my hand, like a curse.

Flor: Is that so? What is the problem?

Sue: I spent a bundle of money, only to find I've bought a stubborn idiot. She ran away, and although we got her back, no matter what we do, she just won't cooperate. Damn, she's like a curse.

Flor: Gee, sounds like you've run into your equal!

Sue: It's not that I can't cure her. It's that I don't want to run the risk of pushing her into suicide. I don't care if she's dead or alive. I just want my money's worth.

Flor: Sue, I might have a way to handle this. Do you want me to get involved in helping you out?

Sue: What method do you have in mind?

Flor: Hey......I am in business longer and have had more experience than you. Just listen closely to me.........

Sue: Good, if you could get her to cooperate, I'll make it very worthwhile for you.

Flor: I don't need your money to thank me, I just want a favor.

Sue: What favor, speak up.

Flor: I am about to reopen my business. I need some "imported" girls. I heard that you have ways of getting them. I could use some for myself, what do you say?

Sue: How do you know that I have imported girls?

Flor: When it comes to this kind of stuff, you might be able to fool the authorities, but not me. As I told you, I'm an old pro.

Sue: All right, count yourself lucky. If you can tame that Jade for me, I'll save two imported girls for you, when I get my next shipment.

Flor: It's a deal. You better not back out of this one.

Sue: If I do, feel free to "Sue" me, O.K.?

Flor: Good! I'll take care of your problem tonight.

Sue: Great! I'm leaving it all up to you now.

(The living room light dims gradually. The left front bedroom light gradually brightens. Rose is throwing up and feeling nauseated. Ann is comforting her)

Ann: Look at you, your face is so pale. Let me take you to the doctor's. I'm sure you must be awfully sick.

Rose: Don't worry Ann, now that it's all come up, I feel much better.

Ann: I noticed that you've been throwing up quite often. You must be careful not to eat anything that is not clean.

Rose: Dear Ann, let me tell you the truth: I'm not sick, I'm pregnant.

Ann: (surprized) What? You're pregnant?

Rose: Yes, it's about two months now. Ann, please don't let Sue know about it.

Ann: Why not? Isn't it a happy thing to have baby?

Rose: Oh, sweet Ann, you are so innocent and naive. Sue definitely does not want us to get pregnant. With a big stomach, how can you do business? No client will want you. It is very bad for business.

Ann: Oh, I see what you mean; but when your stomach starts getting bigger, sooner or later, Sue will find out anyway.

Rose: I know, the important part is to hide it for the first three months. After that, the baby will be too big to get rid of, then Sue has to agree to let me have the baby. This is Ted's baby, I must keep it.

Ann: Ted? You mean the young man who comes to visit you often?

Rose: Yes, that's him. He loves me, and I love him very much too. He promised me that as soon as he finishes his service, he will redeem my freedom and marry me.

Ann: Rose, do you think his parents will let him marry you?

Rose: I hope so. He told me if I carry his baby, his family will have to agree, for the sake of the family name. His family is down South, they have a lot of land. Recently they made a fortune by developing some of it. It should be easy for them to buy my way out of here.

Ann: Oh, I'm so happy for you, pretty soon you'll be out of this hell hole.

Rose: Ann, you must remember, never let Sue find out about my baby.

Ann: I promise I'll never tell. I hope some day, I come out of this as well as you have.

(Suddenly, there is a knock at the door, Sue is yelling)

Sue: Rose, Ann, hurry out here, we have guests!

Ann: Yes, ma'am, right away. (Both straighten out their clothes. Rose opens the door, and both go into the darkness, off the stage. After a while, Flor holding Jade enters the room. Jade uses her hand to cover her eyes, which are not accustomed to the light. Jade is weak, the results of a brutal beating show through her torn clothes.)

Flor: Tch....Tch....Tch, Sue is too cruel, how could she torture you like this? (Tries to help Jade sit still in the chair, touches her arm)

Jade: (screams in pain) Ow!! Don't touch me! Oh........Oh......

Flor: (Gently lifts Jade's sleeves and checks her wounds) Oh! You poor thing, let me put some medicine on those, otherwise they will get infected. (Flor exits, Jade is looking at her own wounds. Flor re-enters with some medication and a bowl of soup. Flor starts putting medication on Jade)

Flor: This ointment is quite good. It's an antibiotic and will sooth the wounds, pretty soon you won't feel much of the pain.

Jade: Thank you, ma'am.

Flor: Don't mention it. I just feel so bad for you. They told me that you haven't eaten for three days, you must be starving. Come on, I got you some soup, drink it while it's hot, it will help you gain some strength back. (Hands over the soup)

Jade: (Holds on to the soup but doesn't drink it) Ma'am, why are you so nice to me? You're helping them to persuade me to succumb, right?

Flor: Jade, how could you think this way?

Jade: I am not here of my own free will. My boyfriend betrayed me and set me up. He abducted me and sold me against my will. I will never be a prostitute. If she lets me go, I'll be eternally grateful. If not, I'll kill myself instead. If I die, I will haunt her forever.

Flor: Jade.........When I heard that they were torturing you, my heart ached for you. That is why I intervened. I had a daughter who died at the age of seven. If she had lived, she would be about your age by now. I feel sorry for you, that's why I asked Sue to spare you from further pain. Drink the soup, get your strength back, and then we will figure out some way to get you out of here.

Jade: You're going to help me out of here?........ How?...... Sue paid that bastard big money for me, she is not going to let go of me easily.

Flor: If you are willing to become my daughter, and let me adopt you, it will be worth any amount. Hurry up, drink the soup while it's hot, come on. (Holds the bowl up to her mouth)

Jade: Thank you! (Just as she's about to drink, she suddenly remembers something) Oh, by the way, where do you live? Who else do you have in your family?

Flor: Oh....... I live not too far from here, a nice residential area. I have only a husband at home, we both are about to retire, if you join us, we will no longer feel lonely........ You can continue going to school, I am sure we would be happy together.

Jade: It's too good to be true! Are you sure you're not lying to me? I've been cheated by too many, I couldn't handle any more lies.

Flor: Jade, I know you're an intelligent girl, a good student. I will take good care of you, trust me. You drink the soup first, then I'll get you something else to eat to get you back to health.

Jade: Thank you, you are very kind. (Jade drinks the soup, bit by bit and finishes)

Flor: That's my good girl! I'll go get you some more food.

Jade: Ma'am, what kind of soup is that? It's very bitter. I........I........for some reason, I feel dizzy.......... What did you put in it? (Jade tries to fight her dizziness)

Flor: What are you talking about? The dizzy spell must be from your lack of food. I'm going to get you something to eat., you wait here. (pretending to leave)

Jade: Oh, my God, what's happening to me...............(Jade falls on the floor and passes out)

Flor: (Walks up and leans over Jade) Jade.......... dear, are you alright?.......... (Jade shows no response) Ha! No matter how stubborn you are, you will never be my match! Ha! Ha! (Clap her hands to signal Sue to come out. Sue enters from one of the left rooms)

Flor: See! What did I tell you? She won't be fighting you anymore now! Get Clint to strip her down. Let's take a set of pornographic pictures using her. From now on she'll have to listen to you.

Sue: Flor, you're a true professional. But what if she still refuses after waking up?

Flor: You've got the pictures and the film. If she fights, tell her that you'll copy the pictures and sell them on the streets, or even send a set of them to her mother as a gift. I can't imagine that she'll be that stubborn!

Sue: Yes! You are right! This is the only trick I can see where she has no choice but to listen to me.

Flor: Good, I'm glad that you like it. Just don't forget what you promised me. (Lights dim)

(lights gradually rise in the living room. Sue is at the desk doing bookeeping. The telephone rings)

Sue: Hello, who is this? Oh, Ed. (Becomes serious and respectful) Yes, whatever you want, just tell me......... You need money? No problem, I'll send our contribution early............You're at your retreat house? The one at the Hot Spring? .... I know where that is................ You need some girls for entertaining? Sure, whatever you say, I'll pick my best girls and have Clint bring them up to you, right away.......... Oh, you are welcome........ For you, I'd do any thing, you know that! Goodbye, I'll see you soon. (Hangs up the phone, and calls out) Clint! Clint!

Clint: (Enters from the left room, getting his clothes on as he walks out) Are you calling me, ma'am?

Sue: Our big boss, Ed, just called; he needs the protection fee early. He also needs some girls at his retreat house to help entertain his friends. Pick our best ones and drive them up now.

Clint: Yes, Ma'am, I'll go right now.

Sue: (Opens a drawer, gets a stack of money and a booklet out) Just a minute, here's the "contribution" for the month, hand it to him and ask him to please sign the book. You think, you can do it right?

Clint: Yes, ma'am, I promise I'll make you proud.

Sue: On your way, warn the girls, that those are V.I.P. customers. Make sure that they know how to entertain those people, and handle themselves, you hear?

Clint: Yes, ma'am I'll tell them.

Sue: All right, you may go now.

Clint: I'm on my way! (On his way out toward the left doors, he suddenly turns around) Oh, by the way, ma'am, just one thing, I wonder whether you're aware or not.............

Sue: What is it?

Clint: (Whispers in Sue's ear)............

Sue: (surprised) How did you find out about that?

Clint: One of our clients told me.

Sue: (Gives some thoughts) You..... You go and get Rose for me.

Clint: Why don't you wait until after we leave.

Sue: No, I want to see her immediately! (Turns to open a drawer and removes a bottle of pills)

Clint: (Hesitates, then moves toward the left rooms) Rose, Madam wants to see you, please come now. (As soon as Rose shows up, Clint leaves the room)

Sue: Rose.........

Rose: Yes, ma'am, you called?..........

Sue: I heard that you are expecting, is this true?

Rose: (Nervously) No, I'm not.......

Sue: No? (Slaps Rose across the face) How dare you lie to me?! Even the clients noticed the difference and told me. How dare you deny it! You fool!

Rose: (Holding her face, crying) I just don't feel that well, how do I know whether I'm pregnant or not?

Sue: Come here, let me check. (Checks her stomach, feels around) You sure are pregnant. Tell me the truth, how far along are you ?

Rose: (Surrendering) I don't know..........May be two or three months. I really don't know for sure.

Sue: I don't care if it's three months or four months. You take this bottle of pills and divide them into three days' dosage to finish it up, you hear me?

Rose: (Starts to cry and beg) Please, let me keep my baby..........

Sue: (Angrily yells at Rose) What?........ Why would you want to keep a baby in this environment anyway? God knows who the father is!

Rose: I know who the father is. It's Ted's baby. He promised me that he is going to marry me, and pay you money to buy my freedom.

Seu: You must be dreaming. How could you take the customer's words seriously? You are better off getting rid of it.

Rose: Oh, no, please, no....... I have always been agreeable, I've always listened and done whatever you wanted me to. This baby, I must keep,it is my way out of here. (on her knees) I beg you, please spare us.......I beg you..........(crying)

Sue: (Loudly) Stop it! I don't give a shit what you say! Don't you know the rules here? I don't allow pregnant women and babies here. Take the pills right now!

Rose: (Starts to cry out loud) Oh Madam, please, I beg you! Oh, dear God, please help me!

Ann: (Ann rushes out from left rooms, gets on her knees too) Madam, I beg you, too, please spare her............

Sue: Ann, you stay out of this. It is none of your business. The rules are here for a good reason. The place will look like shit with

40

pregnant women around. Both of you get up! Your efforts are useless, I can't do business that way. (Two still on their knees, Sue gets mad, raises her voice) What?.......... You two are still fighting against my decision? Get up, (Two of them still on their knees) You choose not to listen?........ All right let me show you........

(Sue goes to get a whip,and is just about to beat them, when Officer Coral shows up at the front door)

Coral: Is any one here?

Rose: Oh, somebody please help me.

Sue: (Rushes up to the police officer, sweetly) Officer Coral, how are you today? Here for another inspection?

Coral: Yes, ma'am. What's going on here?

Sue: Nothing, we were just fooling around playing games- all in fun. Rose, Ann, we'll finish our discussion later. Hurry, get up and tell the girls to open their doors for inspection.

Rose: (Quietly and determinedly) No, if you don't agree to my request, I won't get up.

Sue: (Quietly) You stupid idiot, what are you trying to do? You must have a death wish!

(Ann gets scared and tries to sneak out. Coral spots her and calls out, stopping Ann.)

Coral: Just a minute, who are you? What is your name?

Ann: (scared and quietly) My name is Ann.........

Coral: How old are you?

Ann: I........I......I am eighteen.......

Coral: Eighteen? I don't believe you.......

Sue: (Rushes up to explain) Oh, Officer, she is Rose's old classmate. She stopped by to take Rose out to a movie. All right, Rose, if

you insist, you may go to the movie now. Hurry, don't be late. (Signals them to leave with a nod of her head)

Rose: That's O.K. I don't feel like going anymore.

(Sue looks as if she's about to have a fit)

Coral: Rose, is she really your old classmate? I don't think so. (Turns to Ann) Show me your I. D..

Ann: My.......my I.D. is ....kept by Madam. I don't have it.

Coral: That is exactly what I thought. Obviously, you are a minor. I am sorry, Madam, you'll have to come down to the precinct with me. You too, Ann, you'll tell us the truth over there.

Sue: (Angrily) No big deal! I'll go with you. I am not afraid of anything.

Ann: (gets scared, then starts to cry) I.....I don't want to go, I don't want to go to jail.

Coral: Don't be afraid, it is not your fault, you're not going to jail, I just need you to testify.

(Hearing all the noise, Clint enters from the left room)

Clint: What is going on here?

Sue: Clint, I am going to the precinct with the police. We've had a misunderstanding over Ann. Call Ed for me and ask him to make some phone calls. Do you understand?

Clint: Yes, I understand.

Coral: Come on, let's go.

(All three of them exit through the main entrance)

Lights darken, curtain down

END OF ACT TWO

ACT THREE

Time: Some time after Act two.

Scenery: Same.

Characters: Daisy, Kit, Rose, Jade, Flor, Sue, Happy, Clint, Coral, Young.

When curtain goes up, it is daytime but cloudy. The living room is dark. The left front room light is on. Daisy and Kit are chatting.

Daisy: (Gets out a golden necklace shows it off) Kit, look, isn't this necklace beautiful? Do you have one?

Kit: No, but I have a jade bracelet. (shows Daisy the bracelet)

Daisy: (Takes a look, gives it back to Kit) It's fake, only the real ones are worth anything.

Kit: Sure, just because you don't have one, you say it's fake. Actually you don't really know anything about jade.

Daisy: Never mind.......... Seriously, Kit, did you ever imagine that we could make this much money?

Kit: What's the use? Madam takes it all.

Daisy: Kit, that's just for the moment. She said, at the end of each month, we'll get our share. We could get a couple of thousand dollars. Compared to what we used to make, it's incredible!

Kit: Yes, but I somehow don't feel good about doing this kind of work.

Daisy: As long as I can make good money, who cares?

Kit: If people back at home find out what we're doing here, they'll look down on us. I could never face them without feeling shameful.

43

Daisy: Oh, you think too much. We're so far away, nobody at home will ever know. If we ever have to go back, as long as we don't say anything, who would know?

Kit: Well, somehow, it seems that if you do something wrong, people always find out about it eventually.

Daisy: If you're really worried about it, why don't we just stay here for good, and not ever go back to that God forsaken place.

Kit: We'll see. By the way, I have been having some pains down there.......... I heard that V.D. is hard to cure, and also some thing called AIDs, if you get it you die. Is that true?

Daisy: No, where did you hear such nonsense? AIDS is a disease for homosexuals only, not us.

Kit: Are you sure about that?

Daisy: Of course I'm sure, why would I lie to you?

Kit: Anyway, I've just been feeling some pain and itching down there. It's weird.

Daisy: You worry too much. Just use some soap, give it a good scrub, and it'll go away.

Kit: All right, I'll give it a try.

Daisy: One of my clients said that I have a very nice body, and that I should try the "Body Show". All you have to do is dance topless on a runway and show people your body. You make good money, do you want to give it a try?

Kit: Sure, but how? We're strangers in town, we don't know where to go.

Daisy: That client told me that he has a friend who owns an "Opera House", it specializes in the porno "Body Show". They are always looking for new blood with nice figures. He said the pay is over ten thousand each show, it's way better than here, how about it?

Kit: Sounds fabulous, but there is no way that Madam will let us leave here, and work somewhere else.

Daisy: That guy said he could try to help us to sneak away from this joint.

Kit: It's not that simple. You know, we're constantly being watched. Furthermore, we don't know anybody here, what if it doesn't work out? We'd have nowhere to return to.

Daisy: (Thinks it over) Kit, maybe you're right, we better think it over carefully before we do anything. Gee......Kit, you're smarter than I thought.

(A knock on the door, a voice says: Daisy, Kit, come out. We have some guests here for you)

Daisy: Damn, we don't even get a few minutes rest; we have to work again.

Kit: People here are loaded, they seem to have so much money and are eager to spend it.

(As they are talking, they ready their makeup and clothing. They leave the room and go into the dark living room off stage).

(A while later, Jade brings Rose into the room, closes the door. Rose sits down and starts to cry again)

Jade: Rose, I am so sorry. Please don't cry. It is done, crying will not help; you ought to take care of yourself.

Rose: Jade, you don't know how much I cared about this baby. It was made of Ted's and my love. With the baby, Ted and I had a chance to persuade his parents. Now the baby is gone, I don't know whether Ted will still marry me.

Jade: Come on, don't worry. If he really loves you, he will marry you, regardless. You are young, you will have as many babies as you want.

Rose: I've got a feeling that after this, Ted and I will be hopeless. (Starts to cry again)

Jade: Stop crying, Rose. You make me feel like crying too...........

Rose: I can't understand it. Madam is a woman too, why is she so harsh
and cruel? She doesn't want a baby, but why can't she let
others have one? Oh, dear God, what kind of world is this?

Jade: This is an unfair world. This is a dog eat dog world. Some people
are worse than animals; they will do anything for money. They
suck your blood like Dracula, I hate this world, I hate myself for
even bothering to live in this world.

Rose: Jade, stop it. Your case is unusually vile. I could not believe that
any human being could do such vicious things. I don't even
know what to say............I am so sorry for you. It is so sad and
so cruel. (Hugs Jade and tries to comfort her)

Jade: Those blood suckers set traps everywhere in order to catch their
pry and feed upon them. How could I be so naive..........When I
think about what I have to face in the future, I lose the courage
to live.   I really don't know how long I can take this humiliation.

Rose: Jade, don't even think about it. It is not your fault. It just
happened that you fell into a snake pit, you are surrounded by
them, consumed by them. It just happened ,that you had a vile
boyfriend abduct you and sell you, that you had a mean woman
running this place and a cruel rattlesnake to drug you and set
you up. The way I look at it, they all have to pay for their sins in
Hell. Don't you let the hatred rot your soul. Try to endure your
life, and make the best out of the worst. I have already mailed
your letter for you, you should be rescued soon.

Jade: Rose, how long is your contract here?

Rose: Three years. I have worked one year. If Ted doesn't redeem me,
I have two more years before I get my freedom.

Jade: How did you get here?

Rose: It is a long and sad story. My parents died when I was very
young. My grandmother raised me by selling cigarettes at a
booth. She died when I was only fourteen, too young to take
care of things. A distant relative sold me to pay for the funeral.
For a year, I worked at that Bar House as a maid. When I turned
fifteen, they forced me to wait on customers. Some times they

made me do it in the nude; when I refused, they threatened me with a knife. I had no place to go, no one to turn to. In order to live, I had no choice but to obey them.

Jade: God, that's awful. How did you wind up here?

Rose: Two years later, when I turned seventeen, my owner leased me to a "Call Girl Station" that procures prostitutes for tourists staying in hotels..

Jade: That is so sad. Oh, my God.......

Rose: Later on, they took me to a tourists' attraction to work as a "Massage Girl", but in reality it was just a different form of prostitution. Because I tried to escape a few times, they decided to get rid of me by selling me to Sue for three years. I was so tired of the torture on my body and soul, I was going to end my life soon. Luckily, I ran into Ted. He loves me, comforts me and gives me the strength and the reason to live...........

Jade: You feel sad for me, but I feel more sympathy for you. We both are the victims of those thugs and greedy pimps. We have nobody to turn to, I really don't see any future for us.........(Starts to cry)

Rose: Come on, don't cry, you have me now. We could be sisters. From now on, I am going to call you big sister, all right?

Jade: Oh, you are so sweet, other than being a few months older than you and having stayed in school longer, I don't really qualify to be your big sister. How could I take care of you? I couldn't even survive on my own................ (Both of them hold on to each other and cry, the lights dim)

(Living room lights gradually come on. Sue is idly sitting there snacking, having a cup of tea. Flor comes in from outside with another set of fancy clothes on)

Flor: Is the Madam of the house around?

Sue: Oh, my goodness, Flor, come in, have a seat and join me. (Pours her a cup of tea and puts food in front of her)

Flor: Thank you, but sit; I'll help myself. I am here to check with you about the thing that we talked about last time.

Sue: What thing?........ Tell me, I might forget if you don't remind me.

Flor: Well, how is that Jade doing?............ Has she been cooperative?........... Has she been giving you any more trouble?

Sue: Oh, Jade, she has been wonderful. She is quite popular here. Oh, yes, yes, I am very grateful for what you have done for me. Now I remember, you are wondering about when I can get you those two "Imported girls" right?

Flor: Yes, you remembered, I have been anxiously waiting. When do you think you can get them?

Sue: Flor, don't you worry. I have mentioned this to my source, who has been quite busy lately. He told me to give him two more weeks and he will bring me a few more. Be patient, you will get them as soon as I have them.

Flor: In that case, I am not going to worry. I just wanted to remind you so that you don't forget about me.

Sue: Oh, dear, I'll never forget about you. By the way, this is a very touchy subject politically. You must keep it a secret. If the authorities find out, we not only have no profits to gain, but we might wind up in jail, you hear?

Flor: Of course, who would fool around with money making opportunities? By the way, has Ann's father been here to borrow money lately?

Sue: You mean that old fool? I have not seen him since they took Ann and set her free. I was just about to find him and settle the score.

Flor: Forget it, you can kiss him good by. He is in the "Hotel" now, room and board all free.

Sue: He is in jail? What happened?

Flor: He went crazy over his gambling debt. He even kidnapped
somebody's kid and asked two hundred million for
ransom............

Sue: Then he got caught and wound up in jail?........That damn old
idiot.

Flor: He got quite a few years. He is fine in jail, but those kids............

Sue: Don't worry, no one will starve to death in this town, they always
can come to us to earn a living, right?

Flor: You are right, Ha....Ha....

(Both laughing, telephone rings, Sue picks it up, Flor starts eating
some food and drinking her tea)

Sue: Yes, this is the place. Who are you looking for? Rose? She is
busy........... what? ....urgent? You are at the train
station?..........All right, I'll get her for you, hang on.........(Put
down the phone and goes toward left rooms yells out for Rose)
Rose, telephone, hurry up!

Flor: (Gets up) I better get going now. I'll stop by and see you some
other time. And don't forget about your promise.

Sue: Don't worry, I won't. Come any time.

(Flor exits off stage from the main entrance. While they are saying
goodbye, Rose comes out)

Rose: Thank you Ma'am. (Picks up the phone) Hello, Ted! Where are
you?..........What?...........Your Dad? No?...........I am not good
enough for you.........? You have to go home?.............Why?
How Can I forget...........? Go, go right ahead..........(Starts to
cry) Goodbye.......Ted.....I love you.........Oh, my
God......(Hangs up the phone and cries out loud)

Sue: I knew it, most men are like that, don't say that I didn't warn you.
Don't even bother to cry.

Rose: It is all your fault. You forced me to abort my baby. Ted won't forgive me for that, now I've lost everything, my baby, my love, my chance of being free, and you would even let me cry..........

Sue: (Yells back) That's right, you are not allowed to cry here. No one is dead here, the crying will bring bad luck to my place. Who in his right mind will spend money to come here for tears and sad faces. Go straighten youself out, I have a business to run here.

Rose: All right, have it your way. (Runs off toward left rooms)

Sue: (Angrily, loudly) Jesus, look at your manners. Damn, one of these days I will straighten you all out! (goes off to left room)

(Pete rushes in from outside, looks nervous, calls out for Sue)

Pete: Sue, Sue........

Sue: (Comes out from left room) Pete! haven't seen you for a few days, how have you been?

Pete: (In a hushed tone of voice) Sue, do you have any secret rooms that I can hide out for a few days?

Sue: Why? What has happened? Someone going after you?

Pete: We are in deep shit. The Customs Official found and confiscated the firearms that we smuggled in. When they arrested my boss, fortunately, I was quick; I got away. I need your help. (Get's out a handgun, gives it to Sue) Here, can you hide this gun for me? If you don't have a place for me to hide, I'll go down south to wait it out.

Sue: (Pushes the gun away) You better keep it. I have too many people coming through here every day to keep any secrets. There is no way you can be safe here, let me think..........(Sue opens her drawer to get out a stack of money) I have some money here, take it with you. It should last you for a while. Contact me later, if you need anything........

Pete: (Puts money in his pocket, and sticks his gun in his waist, hugs Sue) Thank you for everything, if I survive this time, I'll come back and catch up with you Babe! Goodbye!

Sue: You take good care of yourself.

Pete: Oh, remember to tell the two stowaways to be more careful. You better not let them go out for the time being. The authorities are suspicious and are looking for their kind.

Sue: Oh, Is that so? I'll be careful.

Pete: I better use your back door, so long.

Sue: So long, see you soon, I hope.

(Pete off stage, from left rooms. A few minutes later, phone rings, Sue picks up the phone)

Sue: Hello, this is she.......... Oh, Bob...of Diana Hotel....... Yes, the same one again? Same price, right? all right I'll send her over right now, room number is........ 707. Thank you!

(Sue hangs up the phone, rings the bell for Clint)

Clint: (Comes in from main entrance) Yes Ma'am. You called?

Sue: Bob of the Diana Hotel called. Apparently the man who had Kit last night wants her back again. You tell her to get ready and you take her there yourself.

Clint: Yes Ma'am, I'll go and tell her.

(Clint goes off on left, Sue tidies up the living room, soon Kit comes out followed by Clint)

Kit: Madam, I don't want to take care of that customer again, is that all right?

Sue: That client liked you last night, and specifically named you again. Why do you refuse to make more money?

Kit: That guy is filthy and dirty. He is a sadist, he loves to hit, you see what he did to me last night. (Kit shows Sue the wounds on her legs)

Sue: If you carefully waited on him, he wouldn't do that.

Kit: That vile bastard, he wanted me to do all kinds of sick and weird things. He tortured me when I refused, I was scared to death. There is no way that I ever want to see him again.

Sue: Kit, are you really refusing to go?

Kit: Yes, I am not going.

Sue: (Angry and yelling) You...... You dare fight against me? Let me tell you, you are going, no matter what. If you say no, I'll beat you until your skin is in shreds.

Kit: I don't care; I am not going.

Clint: Come on, Kit, let's go.

Kit: You go ahead, I am not going. Can't you understand? I am not going?

Sue: Clint, go and get me the whip.

Clint: Yes, Ma'am. (Brings Sue the whip)

Sue: You still are not going, right? I am going to beat you until you beg to go.

(Sue whips Kit, while she tries to duck and hold her hands up to fight the whip)

Klt: Please, can't you send someone else? Tell him that I got sick, why are you doing this?

Sue: Clint, hold on to her, don't let her get away. Today, I am going to make an example out of you even if I have to kill you. I am getting sick and tired of people defying me.

(Clint holds Kit for Sue, while she is just about to beat Kit, Kit is screaming and struggling. Daisy comes out from the left rooms)

Daisy: Stop! ....Madam, something horrible has happened.

Sue: (Stop the action with Kit) What? What is going on?

Daisy: Jade.....She hanged herself in her room......

Sue: What? Jade hanged herself? Clint, hurry up, go check, see whether we can revive her or not.

Clint: Yes, Ma'am. (hurries off into left rooms)

Daisy: (Checking Kit) Kit, what happened to you?\

Sue: There is a customer who liked her, asked for her again, and she dares to say no.

Kit: (Starts to cry) Daisy......You don't know how terrible that man was. He did all kinds of sadistic things to me. He didn't even treat me like a human being. I have never been treated like this in my whole life.........

Daisy: Kit, I know, but somehow you still should listen to Madam.

Sue: Daisy, you are the smart one. You tell her, fighting against me will not get her anywhere but only more pain.

(Clint comes out from left rooms)

Clint: Madam, I could not revive her, she has been dead for a while.

Sue: Damn, It is my luck. I spend four hundred thousand for her, I haven't even made a handful back, and she is dead. Everything is going down the drain.

Clint: Do you want me to report this?

Sue: Report to whom? I don't need any more trouble here. Not a word mentioned to the outside. Tonight, when it is dark, Clint you put her in a bag, tie it to a big rock and throw her into the river. Do you understand?

Clint: Yes, I know.

Daisy: What made her want to kill herself?

Sue: Who knows? She has all the things she needs here, and she still doesn't want to live. I guess some people just prefer being dead.

(Officer Coral suddenly appears)

Coral: Who killed herself? And who prefers being dead?

Sue: Oh, officer Coral, I was just carrying on a conversation with my girls about life in general.

Coral: You have a regular customer named Pete, have you seen him today?

Sue: No, I haven't seen him for a while, are you looking for him? Anything special?

(Sue notices that Daisy and Kit are there, she tries to signal them out, but they don't see her)

Coral: He is wanted for questioning. He really didn't show up here today?

Sue: If you don't believe me, go ahead and search for yourself. (turns to Daisy and Kit)   There is nothing for you to do here, you two may go now. (When they leave and are just about to go into the left rooms, Coral notices they are strangers)

Coral: (Staring at them) Just a minute, who are you? Where are you from?

Daisy: I......I.......

Coral: And you?.........

Kit: We are from south..........

Coral: How old are you?

KIt: I was born In 1972........

Coral: These two talk strange, I bet they are the stowaways. Please show me their I. D.s.

Sue: Officer Coral, we have known each other for a long time. Let's be frank, you are right, these two are stowaways. If you help me out, here is your share......(Opens the drawer and gets out a stack of money; hands it to Coral) to show my appreciation. How about it?

Coral: I am sorry, I can't go along with you. All three of you come with me to the precinct.

Sue: All right, I'll go with you. Clint, you look after everything here until I come back!

(Coral takes all three of them off through main entrance)

Clint: Gee, as the saying goes, if you walk in the dark long enough, you are bound to run into ghosts.

Rose: (Comes in from the left rooms with two letters in her hand) Clint, where is the Boss?

Clint: The police took her, Kit, and Daisy to the precinct.

Rose: Is it because of Jade's suicide?

Clint: No, it is because Kit and Daisy are stowaways. They were illegally smuggled in and don't have a license. What you need the Boss for?

Rose: Nothing, I just want to know where she is. I have to go out. Jade left two letters under my pillow. One is for her mother and the other is for her teacher. I am going to mail these letters.

Clint: Jesus, Jade left letters? Madam said that we shouldn't tell any one about Jade's suicide. If you mail the letters, we will have troubles. I think, we ought to just burn these. (Tries to grab the letters)

Rose: (Refuses) No, I can't. I have to mail them for her.

Clint: You better give them to me.........Let me burn them. Come on.

Rose: No, these are Jade's last words. She trusted me with them, I can't let her down.

(While they are arguing and struggling, Ms.Young shows up from the main entrance)

Young: Does Jade live here?

Rose: Who are you? Why are you looking for her?

Young: I am Jade's teacher. Recently I received another letter from her. Apparently she is here suffering and asked me to rescue her out of here.

Rose: Oh, My God, you are the teacher that she was telling me about. (Starts to cry) You......You are too late...... She could not handle it any longer.........She hanged herself

(Strong sound effects)

Young: What? Jade is dead? I am too late? No, no, this can't be.

Rose: This is the letter that she left for you, you read it yourself.

(Clint tries to stop her, but is too late. Young takes the letter open it slowly, while Clint gets mad, walks back, pours a glass of wine, walks toward the bay window to look outside. The stage gradually turns all dark, with only one light concentrated on Young and Rose. The letter is read by Jade's voice)

Jade: My dearest teacher: Farewell. As you know, my entire life was chapters of struggling. The poverty didn't stop me from seeking education and improving myself. I have always been a fighter with high morals and self respect. My biggest mistake in life was falling in love with a devil. He cheated my innocence, abducted and sold me here. Although I fought hard, they tricked me,drugged me and blackmailed me into submission. I thought I could live without my soul, out of the love and care for my mother. The mental humiliation and physical torture has broken my spirit. It gave me no reason or hope to continue my life. In school, we learned how to love and be kind, etc. However, we were never told how to distinguish the evil from the good. We were never told that in reality, the world is filled with greedy, vile, and contemptuous people. They prey on the weak and naive ones, drain their blood, and feed on their flesh. My biggest disappointment is that a so called "Advanced Society" with its high technology and economic development,

doesn't even have a system or the ability to protect the poor and the helpless. I don't blame you for not saving me in time. Actually, I don't mind dying. I want to use my death as a voice to protest our society's wrongdoing. I only beg you please to spread my story to the public. I want people to be aware of the cruelty and the darkness of this business. I want my bright red blood to warn the young people about their surroundings. I want people to speak up for change, to improve, to have a healthy society, to reach the needed. With my death, If I can prevent any further tragedy like mine, I feel that my life has been worth something. Your respectful student Jade's last words.

Rose: (By now sobbing) Jade, Oh, you poor thing. How am I going to face my future without your help?...........

Young: Jade, I am so sorry. I am too late to save you, how can I face your mother?

Rose: Ms. Young, this is the letter Jade left for her mother. Please take it with you.

Young: Jade, I'll bring this to your mother. I'll tell the whole world about your encounter. I hope your story will save others, so that your death will not be in vain. (both of them crying. Gradually lights turn bright and they calm down a little)

Rose: Ms.Young, Jade's body is still in the back. Would you like to take a look and say goodbye?

Young: Yes, I would love to. Please take me to it.

(Both of them off into left rooms, Clint is left on stage alone with a glass of wine in his hand leaning against the bay window looking outside. He walks toward the front of the stage, he sits down, take a sip, puts his glass down and folds his arms in front of him and starts thinking ....thoughts come out through sound effects and the lights gradually darken)

Clint: Jade's body..........I better consult with Ms. Young. I don't really want to throw her into the river.........

(Lights gradually turn bright, Jade is on stage, standing in front of Clint)

Jade: Clint..........Clint........

Clint: (Scared to death, tries to walk away, but is too frightened to get up. He is backing away in the seat, putting his hands up) Oh...... Jade! .... You.........You killed yourself. I.......I......I didn't have anything to do with it..........Those pictures...........is the Boss.....Made me do it......... Flor........ Flor's idea..........Spare.....me

Jade: (approaching him step by step) You helped her with all the crimes, I will not forgive you........ I am taking you with me..........(By now Clint is curled up in the seat with his hands holding his head. Jade gets ahold of him)

Clint: Let go of me........Please........have mercy.......(Screaming, the lights totally darken for a few seconds, giving Jade a chance to leave the stage, and for Sue to replace her. When the lights are bright again, Sue is in front of Clint pulling his sleeve while he is sleeping on the seat screaming and struggling) Let go of me..........Please........

Sue: Wake up, Clint, what is the matter with you?

Clint: (Wakes up startled) Oh, it is you, Boss.

Sue: Look at you, what nightmare did you have? You scared me half to death.

Clint: I dreamed of Jade, she came for me...........

Sue: What are you afraid of ? She killed herself, you didn't do it.

Clint: I really saw her come for me..........I am not kidding.

(Telephone rings, Sue picks up)

Sue: Hello, this is she.......Oh, Bob................I am sorry, Kit can't come. She has been arrested. Ask your guest whether he will be interested in others...........yes, just give me a call, I'll send some one else...........Thank you. (Hangs up the phone and turns to Clint) By the way, have you done anything with Jade's body yet?

Clint: No......Not yet.

Sue: (thinking for a while) That's it, I don't think we should throw it into the river now. You go and get the funeral home to come get the body first. If the police ask any questions, just deny every thing. After all, we really didn't know her well enough to say anything, right?

Clint: Yes Ma'am. I think this is a much better way of handling it. I'd better get on with it. (Clint exits stage from main entrance)

(Ann comes in from the main entrance)

Sue: Ann, what are you doing here?

Ann: Ma'am............. My Dad is in jail, my brother and sisters are too young, I have no way of getting enough money for food and to send them to school. In order to suport them ....May I work here for you to earn a living?

Sue: You want to come back and work here? What about the money that your father still owes me?

Ann: As long as I am working here, I am sure, one of these days, I will pay it off.

Sue: All right, you poor thing! I'll let you work here.

Ann: Thank you, Ma'am, you are nice......(Tries to say more, but hesitates)

Sue: What is it Ann? Are you hungry? If you are, go to the kitchen and find youself something to eat.

Ann: Thank you Ma'am. (Ann exits stage through left doors)

Sue is the only one on stage. She lights a cigaret, pour herself a drink and sits down on the sofa. She is smoking,drinking and thinking.
The horror music starts, the lights dim, Jade quietly appears in front of Sue.

Sue: Jade, what are you doing here?

Jade: Give me back my life. (Jade grabs Sue's neck and starts to
      strangle her)

Sue: (reaching for her neck) Ahhhh...............

Lights out, curtains down.

End Of Act Three

Translator's Note:

      I was deeply moved by this play. This is not fiction, this is a series of true stories linked together. It disturbed me, because it is happenning now, in a country with a reputation of high moral standards and magnificent culture and civilization. In recent years it has been one of the fastest growing countries in world trade, and has among the highest monetary reserves in the world. I assumed that with a reputation as a model modern dragon, abundance of money and well educated officials, we would have the best and most efficient system in education, social welfare and fine arts, like many small European countries. With such advanced economy, and high tech. , what has gone wrong? Why does this type of tragedy continuously happen? Didn't the children learn in school about common sense and how to protect themselves and where to go for help when in need? What happened to basic decency, morality and religious teaching? Is everyone so busy chasing wealth that they neglect to learn how to handle it after one has obtained it ? Is orgnized crime so powerful that the government has no way of protecting its citizens? Is the trend so degraded that being a prostitute is better off than being poor? I feel ashamed for those who have the power and capabilities to make the society and the system better, but have failed to do so.

      1992 is a presidential election year. Bush and Clinton stress family values in raising the next generation. To me family ties and values are not an issue but a fact of life. You learn how to conduct youself kindly before you go to school. Education is merely to reinforce your skill in surviving, appreciating and enjoying your life. Our family has always tried to be informed and aware of the needs of the needy. We have always been involved in volunteer work and community service. In order to expose my children to the human sufferings and the less perfect side of the mankind, I decided to make this a family project. During the initial translation work, I talked to my youngest daughter, who is a teenager in high school. I wanted to hear her feelings and sentiments about the events in this play due to the closeness of the ages. When the first draft was finished, I asked my son to correct the spelling on the computer. To him it is like playing computer games, full of fun. By participating in the project we all learned that we will never commit any act which is unkind and degrading to another person. I was lucky enough to have my second daughter home on leave from the U.S.Naval Academy for few days.

She had some poetry published and was an award winning actress in her high school plays. I asked her to do the playwright editing, for dialog, stage effects, and the tone of the play.

My oldest daughter, who is an English Major at Williams College in Massachusetts who has won many acclaims for her writing, edited the literary sense of the play. When it was all done, we asked PaPa, the Creative writing minor in his college days, to do the final, Chief editing work. I wouldn't say this is the best work ever. I definitely would say this is a work that combined the best effort, compassion and love of a family, to me it is priceless!

Now, I dedicate this work to my beloved family, especially to John S. for standing behind me for twenty- five years. Happy Anniversary!